HOW TO BUY
AND ENJOY
A SMALL FARM

CONTENTS

RETURN TO THE COUNTRY

Those of us who dream of having a place in the country are caught up in a national phenomenon. Calvin Beale, head of the U.S. Department of Agriculture's Population Study Group, detected the new trend when he studied the census figures. For decades people had been forsaking farms and moving off to cities, searching for jobs. Beale discovered that, in the early 1970s, for the first time in more than 150 years, this trend seemed to be in reverse.

The momentum of the movement back to the land surprised him. Movement was toward the Ozarks of Missouri and Arkansas, into the sunny dry lands of the Southwest, and the green forests of the northern lake country. From New York, Chicago, Los Angeles, and all the metropolitan areas between them, people were scouring the countryside seeking a piece of rural America for their own. In a recent study prepared for the federal government we read that "Owning recreational property is no longer a luxury limited to upper-income families." Today one American family in 12 owns such property, although admittedly, not all of them farms.

Our roots may reach deeper into the land and its husbandry than we suspect. The fact that so many people are either searching for rural property or already own it is convincing evidence that the drive to own land is a strong one. In part this may be an expression of an innate urge to stake out and defend territory. Lesser animals have these territories which they mark in a variety of ways and which they may defend against others of their kind, and there is no reason to believe that we are so far up the evolutionary ladder that we do not share this instinctive drive. There is in many of us a deep desire to control a piece of land. The more the plasticized, neon-lighted trappings of civilization surround us, the deeper becomes this desire to escape. I admit readily that I enjoy owning land because I like to walk over it and feel that I own it. Here on this piece of hill country I can come and go as I like.

Civilization really began when man moved from hunting animals and gathering fruits and berries to growing his own crops. This might have begun where wild seed, gathered for family food, spilled on fertile earth, produced a crop, and awakened people to the potential of planting seed themselves. The young of wild animals, kept as pets, adapted to domestic living and perhaps became the foundations of livestock kept and bred to meet human needs. Agriculture grew as a way of life because the people who farmed lived better. From tools of stone and sharpened sticks, farmers graduated, in time, to wheeled vehicles pulled by beasts of burden, then driven by engines. The rural workman's productivity increased marvelously and fewer and fewer people were needed to produce the food and fiber for all. Populations grew and the young were pushed, by economic necessity, off the land and into the growing cities.

But the old ties to the land, latent and suppressed, were still there hidden in the dreams of the city dweller. All that was needed to set the reversal in motion and start people back to the land was an element of economic independence coupled with a growing urgency to escape the hassle of city living.

Deep within many of us, whether we realize it or not, may be the values which Thoreau celebrated. Although not always articulated, this need for space is widespread. As the works of man —cities, highways, power lines, roaring engines and foul air— close in around us, this longing surfaces, driving people from the cities into the rural areas, seeking what they have lost.

Your tax consultant, insurance consultant, CPA, or stockbroker

The old meets the new in this farmer's use of a doubletree welded to a post as a hanger for his mailbox. The milk can is filled with concrete to provide equilibrium.

may try to dissuade you from buying country property. I happened to mention my plan to buy a farm one day when talking with my highly knowledgeable tax attorney and realized at once that he was cool toward the idea. So was my insurance man. This is easy enough to understand because these professionals are not accustomed to dealing in real estate. Their modeling clay is dollars. I once asked one of them, "Why is it that people in your business don't like this farm idea?"

His answer was quick in coming. "It's non-income producing, and diminishes your economic flexibility because the money is not quickly available. What did you buy it for? You bought it because you thought the value of land would appreciate."

"I bought it for the hell of it," I answered. "I like the place." His face brightened a little. On this basis the idea could be related to the new Porsche he had just purchased. Of course, my reasons were not quite as simple as that. I did indeed expect the value of the place to increase as it already has and probably will continue to do. But I don't expect to realize the profit from it.

We look for property in the country and we talk of economic benefits, appreciating real estate values, the price of saw logs and the value of a beef raised on our own place. But who can measure the value to body and mind refreshed by time spent in the fields and woods, or know quantitatively what this enrichment adds to productivity, a sense of well-being, or even length of life?

CHAPTER
2

WHY BUY AN OLD FARM?

Gradually one becomes a part of the place, discovers its past, and fits into its patterns. We walk over the acres at Spoon Hollow and speculate about the occupants of long ago. We have seen an old map in the county seat which showed us that a hundred years ago there was not one, but two sets of buildings on our place. Besides the house we now use, there was another up the hill about where the little meadow is today. We try to figure out where this vanished house might have stood and talk of bringing the metal detector to help find the spot. There is little to be gained by knowing its exact location except we will put into place one more piece of the history of human use of these acres.

Beyond the meadow, where we follow the narrow trail of foxes and deer, we come to a field carrying the scars of healing gullies. Once, perhaps half a century ago, this field was plowed. The farmer, according to the old records, one D. Sharp, followed his team up and down the slope, turning furrows that might better have followed the contours. A thousand furrows helped speed the water and the thin topsoil down the slope to Spoon River.

Those were years when farmers often mined the soil. This was especially true of hill land farmers here on the edge of Appalachia. Cash was scarce, and families survived by what they could mine from the land. Year after year the hills turned yellower, and the harvests grew smaller.

The edge of this slowly healing field is a fitting place to consider what this country must have been like before white people came this way. Forests everywhere. I have seen old pictures of the woods before the saw and ax touched them. In the Brush Creek bottomlands, two miles to the east, were rich stands of beech forests where the gray giants produced tons of nutritious nuts that fed the bears, turkeys, and passenger pigeons. All of them gone now. On the ridges beyond us grew the oak-sugar maple forests. But on these slopes above the trickling waters of Spoon River, which is really only a creek flowing down to Brush Creek, stood the forests known to the botanists as mixed mesophytic, because they contained such a variety of species. There you would have found giant maple trees with spreading arms; towering tulip trees with trunks reaching straight up for a hundred feet; tough old oaks that were destined to become beams in pioneer barns and boards in the floors of farm homes. But always there were the chestnut trees, spreading giants that year after year produced a dependable crop of nuts to fatten the bears, turkeys, squirrels, and deer. The chestnuts were often the dominant trees in the mixed mesophytic forests, but the blight carried by imported chestnut trees found these natives without resistance to the foreign pathogens. And the chestnuts, spreading and otherwise, are now gone, or nearly so, from these hills.

The forests that once stood here on the slopes above Spoon River grew so tall that the land beneath them was forever in deep shade. The earth was cool, and mats of leaves and forest humus sponged up the falling rain, retained it, and fed clear water slowly into the watershed.

The Shawnees lived from the surplus of this land. Then came the hunters and trappers—the woodsmen. But Daniel Boone, Simon Kenton, and Neil Washburn—those combination explorers and Indian fighters—were followed by farmers who cut and burned the oaks, maples, chestnuts, and beeches to make room for corn, cattle, and their families. Our old place here at Spoon Hollow was once known as the Washburn farm. Neil Washburn's brother was one of my ancestors, so perhaps he plowed these hills, or, if not, other hills not far from here.

The weekend farm, with its old house and gardens, offers its owners a change of pace and an opportunity to put aside city problems.

Then came D. Sharp and others, all of them taking from the land more than they gave to it. But I cannot find it in my heart to blame these early people for mining the soil. The problems they faced followed their descendents down the years. I remember them well for my own father faced similar struggles feeding his family from eroded hills during times of economic stress.

But the turn-around years were coming to rural America. The worn-out little family farms were abandoned by people moving to cities to live in the shadow of the factories where they worked. The hills where I once helped my father grow corn and little patches of soybeans, quickly reverted, once abandoned, and grew up to thick stands of brush, and then trees that reclaimed the slopes.

Farmers became big operators, combining small holdings into larger farms. Fences could be removed and fields combined to make long rows where heavy, modern plows, planters, and combines could drive on and on, without having to make a hundred sharp turns a day. Agribusiness had replaced family farming.

There are still family farms where people milk cows, grow corn and hogs, and raise sheep and cattle. But the agricultural economists tell us that the most efficient grain and livestock farms today are three-man operations. Each person can do the work on more than 300 acres, making the 1,000 acre farm operated by three workmen perhaps the most efficient unit. There is a world of difference here from 120 acres supporting a couple and their children.

Often the modern farmer and his family do not live on the land. Instead they have a house in a town nearby, and the farmer travels each day to work in the country.

But many who left the land are finding their way back. With them are many more who, even though they never worked the soil, long for country living and an escape from city pressures. Perhaps man, despite his cities and neon and plastic, is still, first and last, a product of the soil, the air, and the sunshine.

A small farm can be therapy for both body and spirit. Clean air, pure water, physical exercise, and the quiet of the country sends the weekend farmer back to the city refreshed. And for those who can live full-time on their small farms, the country atmosphere becomes a soothing tonic prompting the frequently heard declaration, "I wouldn't move back to town for anything." When we head for Spoon Hollow, we leave behind the cars and trucks that move incessantly along the streets and highways; the background noise of airplanes and trains; the pressures of demanding jobs that bind us to the metropolis; the city air pollution index for the day; and news of chemical spills into the public water supply.

The farm is fun. It may be my last toy. We keep a canoe in the country because two miles from us a fine, clean, little stream rolls down through the green hills, and we float it whenever we can. If your farm has a pond, this water can be used for fishing and swimming or a place for the family to hold picnics on the

The place in the country becomes a favorite with family pets as well as with the human members.

Among the pleasures of spending time on your own country place are the planting and tending of flowers.

Pursuit of hobbies connected to the land is an attraction for many of the people who become owners of rural land.

shore. For those who take photographs, paint, or watch birds and other wildlife, the farm, even a small one, can provide rich opportunities.

Land can also be a good investment. Realtors are fond of saying that land is a good buy because "they're not making any more of it, and it is not going to get cheaper."

Land is one of the last things to lose value. During depressions and recessions, its dollar value seldom slips quickly or drastically. This does not mean that all land in every part of the country is a good investment, or that land is a good buy for everyone. Instead it indicates that rural land can be a sound investment if: you really want to own land; the idea is approached wisely; and the individual farm selected is priced right.

The price of highly productive agricultural land has sky-rocketed in recent years. In 1976, *Farm Journal* reported that information gathered from 700 midwestern bankers showed a 27 percent increase in rural land values over the preceding year in Iowa, Illinois, Indiana, Michigan, and Wisconsin. Land values in these states had averaged a 6 percent increase *per quarter* for 12 consecutive quarters. Even recreation land and small farms that are not considered top agricultural property have also been growing in value.

Many purchasers of small farms dream of retiring to the country. Some have previous experience living in rural areas, but many have none. Even those who do should understand that country living has changed drastically in the last half century. They may find heavy traffic on country roads, and much background noise from highways, farm machinery, and aircraft. Even country people now lock their doors.

Those new to country living have no base line experiences for comparison and such changes will not be noticeable. Before build-ing or buying a retirement home in the country you should consider how living away from the city will differ from what you have known. Living far from shopping centers requires you to plan trips to town more carefully, to keep a shopping list, and to make sure nothing is forgotten.

Not having close neighbors could disturb some people. Many others who move to the country view this as an advantage. But the adjustment can be difficult for those who must be surrounded by people to be happy. Country people are not a lot different from city people. In some places there is resentment against city people who buy country land. But the newcomer willing to become a part of the community can overcome much of this, forming friendships gradually as opportunities arise.

Make it a point to find out what you can about your rural area. There is probably a daily or weekly newspaper, and either one can bring you closer to the people, the problems of the country, and what is going on there from square dances to concerts. When you buy a farm, you buy into an established community of farms, businesses, and homes. Those new to a community, however, should not jump into community improvement projects immediately. Even in worthwhile campaigns—bringing zoning to the county or fighting some destructive land use project, such as a dam or a watershed channelization scheme—let local people lead. Move gradually into the rural scene and the country community. You will find that country living can bring the owner of a small farm peace and a sense of belonging to the land, a freedom to walk your own acres and re-establish a link with a way of life that was, and still can be, rich, rewarding, and permanent.

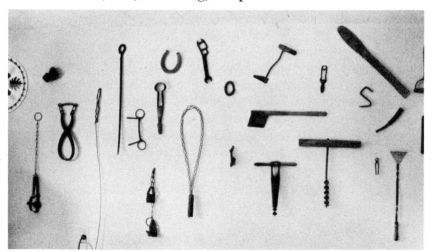

As the antique tools decorating this farm kitchen testify, nostalgia is a strong motivation for many of the people who buy small farms.

CHAPTER

3

FINDING AND BUYING

YOUR FARM

Our earliest efforts to locate a rural property were limited to studying classified advertisements in the Sunday paper. Each week we read through the list of properties offered under "Farms," marking any that looked even close to what we wanted. Many advertisements don't mention the asking price. There are many other important points that can only be learned by talking with the agency listing the property. Agencies are usually open for business on weekends. This is when they get the most calls.

Before calling any realtors it is a good plan to go over the questions you want answered. The following list should help, and you may want to add your own questions to it:

1) How much does the owner want for the property? 2) Will the agent offer him a lower price? 3) Does the property have basic crop allowances, such as a tobacco base, that promises income to the purchaser? 4) What is the land being used for? 5) Are there buildings? 6) Does it have road frontage? 7) Are there creeks or springs? 8) What is the condition of fences? 9) Are there power lines, factories, race tracks, junk yards, or other undesirable neighborhood features that might detract any from its appeal? 10) Is it presently occupied?

11) Does it have timber? 12) What is the condition of lanes leading into it? 13) Are there public utilities available? 14) When can the agent show you the place?

The phone call may save time and expense for both the purchaser and the realtor by answering some of these basic questions. The biggest question is the matter of price, but do not hesitate to ask about other points that might rule the property out from the beginning.

In addition to the Sunday papers and the real estate agent, there are a few other steps that can be taken to locate country property. One of these is the weekly newspaper in the county in which you would like to own land. These papers carry advertisements of the farms for sale. The local paper is also a good source of other neighborhood information, including the names of local politicians, and leading families, as well as those offering services, such as well drilling and electrical work that you might need later on.

A realtor can be a big help in your search for a small farm, but think seriously about what you really want before you phone a realtor.

Word of mouth can also be productive. If you already have friends who are landowners in the area, talk with them. Ask if they know of land available, or if they know local people who might have a line on farms the owners would consider selling.

Some city people enjoy spending their Sunday afternoons cruising rural roads investigating the "For Sale" signs. We watched for them too, and, on more than one occasion, wrote down telephone numbers and made calls to the agents. It is a better plan to call the agent than the owner. But those long rides in the country in the hope of finding a suitable property for sale are usually a waste. You will not know the region as well as the professional real estate agents who live and work there. You will miss many good possibilities simply because you cannot cover the entire area. Besides, the agent will take you in his own car and this is part of his cost of doing business.

Occasionally an owner will not offer his own property through a realtor, hoping to keep the entire profit for himself. The inexperienced buyer, however, will probably do better to work through an agent. The agent's commission comes out of the seller's money. He wants the sale to go through as much as the buyer, so he can often help the purchaser in many ways, recommending people who offer various services and arranging finances whenever needed.

The newspaper search will sooner or later lead to properties that you want to inspect. Then you can make an appointment to meet the agent in his office. We talked with several real estate agents. Some of them seemed eager to help us find what we wanted; others made minimum effort.

One agent took us out to see a 50-acre hillside farm which, according to him, was exactly what we were looking for. Overall, we found the place did have some attractive features—the hills were nice and the little white house acceptable. But the woods, which I felt to be an important factor in our final choice, consisted of a thin stand of old trees.

Our final decision was not to make an offer. Later on, we discovered that the agent apparently decided that we had not been serious buyers. The next time I called about another advertised property, I spoke with his wife who asked, "What was wrong with the other one he showed you?" Because I had already explained to the agent himself what was wrong, I reached the conclusion that we were not operating on the same wavelength. I never called him again, but the property we finally bought was only a few miles from the one he failed to show us.

Once you have made contact with a real estate agent who specializes in country property and is willing to work with you, you have made a major step in the right direction. But be certain he is a specialist in rural property. You know this to be the case if his advertisements offer predominantly rural property week after week. A city real estate agent, or one dealing in city business properties, will be of little help.

You should also determine if the agent belongs to a multi-listing real estate association. This could give you a much wider choice of properties. Under this arrangement many realtors list their properties with each other and sell each other's properties, splitting the commissions.

One Sunday we found several interesting properties advertised by an agency in the county seat of the adjoining county. This was the area in which we were most interested, so I called the realtor and asked about the properties for which we marked the advertisements in the paper. We met him, by appointment, the following Saturday morning at his office and from there rode in his vehicle out into the country.

He enjoyed showing country property and just being out in the rural area. His vehicle was a comfortable four-wheel-drive job with a winch on the front, an arrangement that would get him into, and out of, any place a four-wheeled vehicle might go. We went down old logging roads and country lanes I would not have driven over with my own car, even if I had known they were there.

There were five places he wanted to show us that morning. This was his usual procedure. He would try to learn what kind of place the potential customer really wanted, then go over his lists to see what he could show them. We talked about the price range, the fact that we wanted some woods, that we would look at a farm either with or without buildings if it met our other requirements. Like everyone, we would be especially interested if a place within our price range had some source of water on it, perhaps a creek.

We soon began keeping a log of places inspected, with notations on acreage, particular features of the farm, prices, and conditions of structures. Another important factor to take into consideration is how far various farms are from your home. Driving distance can be an important factor in determining how much you will use your farm. As you go farther out into the country the land prices may be lower than they are close to town. Studies have shown that most people searching for country property who do not plan to move out to it soon, want to be within two hours' drive of their homes in town. With petroleum prices rising, and fuel perhaps becoming difficult to obtain in the future, this distance factor could become increasingly important.

The first place we visited that morning had a big power line crossing the yard. I was not interested. The agent, with his best grin, said power lines had to cross somebody's land. We went on to the next place. One by one we found conditions that ruled each of them out. By the end of the morning we were no closer to a choice than we had been. But the agent did not seem discouraged. A week later he was showing us another half a dozen properties.

Remember that your idea of what constitutes a fine view or a good woodlot may vary considerably from those of the real estate agent. One agent, to whom we mentioned our desire for a wooded area, drove us into the country to see a property he had listed that was all woods. We walked onto the property only to find ourselves crawling over the brush and broken limbs left by a recent logging operation. The logging machinery had cut the place into gullies. The area was a wasteland—walking through the tangle of limbs and brush was almost impossible. All the trees of value had been hauled off to the mill. There was said to be more than 100 acres in the property and I asked the agent if it was all in this condition. "Oh no," he replied, "they've just started to log, but whoever buys it has to understand that the present owner has contracted for the rest of the timber on the place."

This experience was the result of going out with a real estate agent who did not have many rural properties to show and who was not working with other agents. We learned that it is best to work with those who can show you a wide selection. Going down the list you can pick out those of the approximate acreages and price you want, and get a preliminary line on their major features, including buildings, water, and road frontage. In this way you can narrow the list to the five or six you can probably inspect in one day.

More than once the realtor had mentioned one farm he thought we would like. Each time, I told him that the asking price made it well beyond what we were going to pay. Then one evening, after he had made many trips with us over several weeks, he phoned. "There's been a change in the price of that place I mentioned with all the woods and the pond," he said. "The owner has decided that he has to sell, and he put the price way down." I asked him how far down. I also thought we might divide it and buy half of it, so we drove out with him to see it. That was how we came to our hollow after seeing perhaps 20 or 30 other farms.

There is no reason to work with only one real estate agent. If you want to see what is on the market, you will probably have to check with more than one.

Beware of the salesman who tries to sell you a "baby farm," or a piece of land that is really a fraction of a bigger property someone has divided into parcels for resale. Somebody has already paid the market price for this land, and the price you pay for your "baby farm" will be inflated far beyond the actual per-acre value. These developments are often seen along country roads with a sign on each parcel telling the size of the individual plot and the price as well as the financing arrangements possible.

Typical is a four- or five-acre plot priced at close to $10,000 with perhaps $90 down. The low down-payment becomes a magnet for buyers who want only enough "place in the country" to provide space for a mobile home and a shelter for a horse. You can do far better scouring the countryside in the company of a reliable real estate agent who is a licensed realtor and knows rural properties and the region in which you are interested. The salesman peddling "baby farms" or lots on a development lake does not even have to be a licensed real estate agent.

Getting Along with Your Realtor

From talking with real estate agents I have found that they, like any group of business people, have their pet complaints about their clients. Generally they keep these feelings well hidden. But by understanding how the agent thinks, you can establish a better relationship with him, and this could become a factor in helping you find just the right property.

Country real estate agents are often cut from a different pattern than the high pressure sales people who sell city property. "I realize that I could probably sell a few more properties than I do by applying more pressure," one agent specializing in country property told me, "but I would rather not have my people make a mistake. This is especially true with young people. I tell them that they should go carefully because this will probably be the most important investment they will ever make."

This agent, who has sold 35 to 40 farms a year for more than a decade, listened carefully to my question, "What are some of the complaints real estate agents have against people who contact them? What do you people gripe about among yourselves?"

"First, we have the people who read the Sunday advertisements and drive out without calling. They pull in here and want somebody to go out with them right away and show them the place. We work by appointment when we can, and the chances are that there's nobody who can go without notice. The people become upset and sometimes abusive, but we can't help it. We have people coming out who have made appointments, and we can't leave them and go with somebody who had no appointment.

"Then there are the people who call and want to go out by themselves and just drive past the place and see if it is what they are looking for," the agent explained. "The seller pays us to show the place, not tell people how to drive past. And we don't want people stopping in there without us and telling the seller that we didn't have time to come out. More important, driving by a place doesn't tell people enough about it for them to make a sound decision one way or the other. They can't tell where the boundaries are, and they can't tell what the remote parts of the farm look like. From the road it may not appeal to them at all, but if they could get a thorough introduction to the farm it might be just about what they are looking for. We much prefer to go with them because we know the place and can introduce them to it properly."

Other potential buyers will arrive for an appointment, and the agent finds they have brought along all their relatives and friends who wanted to get out for a Sunday afternoon drive in the country. There will be so many they can't even go in one car, so they will want to follow the agent with a second car.

"I have just about quit going out under those circumstances," the agent told me. "There are several reasons why this doesn't work. You want to stop beside the road, and you must have space for two cars. You want to drive back a rough country lane, and the other car can't go where my vehicle will take me. Every time you stop, you look like a tour leader, standing beside the road explaining to a whole group of people where the line fences are."

"Besides, the real estate agent needs to get acquainted with his buyers. We do this as we ride along, and the more people there are, the less you can learn about the ones supposed to be interested in buying a property. We have to find out, at some point, how much of a down-payment they are thinking about, and a little about their financial status, because these things determine what kind of property they should be looking at, or if they are in a position to buy at all. And there is no way you can bring up such points in a crowd including the buyers' cousins and neighbors."

Real estate agents also dislike the fact that people will insist on looking at properties they could not possibly afford. The realtor's time is limited. Hours spent showing properties beyond the reach of the buyer is time lost. You will get along better with your real estate agent if you tell the truth about your finances.

"We also get people, calling in response to a newspaper advertisement, who refuse to give us a name or address. Everyone is plagued by junk mail from being on mailing lists, but we are not going to hound you until you buy something from us, and there's no way we can help you or think about your needs if you won't give us the opportunity to meet you."

When you go looking for a farm, it's a good idea for both man and wife to make the trip with the agent.

"We have cases," explained the realtor, "where we spend all day with a man, and at the end of the day he says, 'I'll have to bring my wife out,' so you have to spend another day going to the same properties. I suppose they think that they're going to get pressured and that if only one of them comes, they have a way out. And I suppose some real estate agents do use those kinds of tactics. But I'm not going to pressure anyone, because I want them satisfied. That's the only way I'm likely to get their business in the future, and there have been a lot of farms we've sold several times, and a lot of referrals where new customers are sent to us by people we treated right."

But the biggest gripe of all is probably the "no show."

"People will see an advertisement on Sunday that interests them, and they call and want to come out right away," said the agent. "We're filled up for that day, so they make an appointment for another day. About half of them don't show up and don't bother to call and cancel. This usually means lost time.

"Oh, I can tell if they're serious," the agent went on. "You learn to know which ones will probably buy. Two-thirds of those who do not like the first property they came to see end up buying something else. I had a woman call me just this morning. She has been calling me for two years, and I am still trying to find the right place for her because I'm sure she really wants to own a farm."

The agent is not the only one sizing up people. The potential buyer also forms his impression of the agent. There may be an agent he doesn't feel would level with him, or those too quick to pressure him into a decision. There are some bad apples in the lot, as there are in any profession. But if you can find the realtor in whom you have confidence, and both parties approach their dealings honestly and with an open mind, the search for a farm stands a good chance of being both pleasant and productive.

If you're buying a weekend place or a little farm to which you might someday retire, the peace and quiet of the area are important. If it lies in the heart of busy farm country, the background noise may be considerable, day or night. Other sources of noise—including railroads, airports, and highways—should be checked out. The county highway department or a nearby state highway office can tell you about plans underway for new roads through the area.

You should also consider the topography. A mountaintop view may be splendid, but what's the location like in the heart of win-

Bad weather is a good time to look at a farm. If a place looks good in rain or snow, chances are it will look even better in sunshine and warm weather.

ter? Is there a long season when snow and mud make the lane impassable? Or does the land lie in a flood plain where the creek may overflow, cover the road, and isolate you, or perhaps even flood the house you plan to build? These are questions for the owner, realtor, or even the neighbors.

The general appearance of the neighborhood can give you important clues on whether or not you'd enjoy the area and find compatible neighbors. I recall one township road leading through a beautiful wooded valley in which was a farm we considered. But what I recall most vividly is that people in the community had used that roadside as a public dump. Piles of refuse were along the road everywhere, and I probably would never have driven along that road without getting my blood pressure up over the desecration of the landscape.

Also check the zoning regulations. There are still rural sections of this country that have no zoning and may not have any for years to come.

"By God, we don't want nobody tellin' us what we can do and can't do with our own land" is a widespread attitude. And, where there are no zoning regulations, there is precious little the residents can't do, including building a slaughterhouse upwind from your new patio, or starting an auto junkyard or a stock-car racetrack across the road. Zoning regulations, of course, can also control your use of the land.

Before you make a final choice, you may also want to spend enough time in the area to learn all about the traffic past the property. A dusty unpaved road, if it is heavily used, can destroy your peace of mind in dry weather. If possible, see what traffic is like past the place on a Sunday afternoon. Weekends may be the only time you normally spend on your country property, and heavy traffic carrying people to a public lake or other attraction could ruin those weekends with noise. A nearby interstate highway could also fill the nights with the sound of trucks grinding up and down the hills, even if the road is a mile or more away.

Good real estate agents usually know after a few questions and answers what kind of property a potential customer is seeking. Most who want recreational land fall into a pattern.

"I don't know why," says one highly successful agent dealing in rural properties from his Vienna, Missouri, office, "but no matter how much they end up buying, they always start out wanting 40 acres."

This Missouri realtor was nailing up another of his signs when I saw him last. An escapee from the city himself, he understands personally what drives those who come to him seeking country property. People from St. Louis drive the 120 miles out into his Ozark countryside every weekend by the dozens, hoping to discover just the "right" country place they've been seeking for months, maybe years. Even Chicago people come there to drive the back roads and talk with the real estate agents.

This realtor formerly worked in St. Louis himself, fought the daily traffic, suffered the high noise level, and the other features of city living.

"I came out here in 1970 to escape the rat race," he said as he drove a final nail into the sign and leaned back to admire his work.

Then, he attempted to explain the current exodus to the country. "Land," he says, "is better than money in the bank. Land has been increasing in value, and in this area it went up 22 percent last year." This is feeder-calf country, and another major crop is white-oak timber used in whiskey barrel staves. But he warns against moving to the country and hoping to make a living by farming. Most of his city customers, he feels, are not fitted to farming for a living. Instead he says, "Be able to afford what you buy. We shoot square with them, sometimes tell them to go back and get another thousand or so together so they don't have to stretch their resources."

If you're planning to farm your new place for profit, your criteria for making a choice may be different. You will still want to have a place in the country that is pleasant and relaxing when you're not working. With careful research and the help of an expert real estate agent, you may find the property that gives you the right combination of these rural features plus fertile, tillable land. But, depending on how important income from the farm is, you may consider the productivity of the land and its potential for producing crops and livestock the first test of its suitability. Going to the country and picking a run-down, but charming, old abandoned farm for your agricultural enterprise could be a serious and basic mistake. Whoever farmed it before you probably already failed to make the place pay or he wouldn't have given up.

Consider the surrounding farms. A farm community reflects the productivity of the land. The fertility of the soil is the basic foundation for any farming enterprise. By driving through the country, you can often pick out the areas where the soil is fertile simply by studying the condition of the buildings and fences and the appearance of the fields and livestock. Farmers who live in productive areas take pride in their land and have money to spend to keep their buildings well-maintained. Regions with only run-down buildings can reflect the infertility of the soil.

This does not mean, however, that run-down land can never be put back into production. You may like the challenge of rebuilding an old place and renovating the hillside pastures. Such work can be and has been done time and again, and the original low purchase price of the land may be an argument in its favor.

But such farm operations involving renovated pastures usually concentrate on livestock production. If you dream of becoming a producer of cash grain crops, you should study what has happened in commercial agriculture in recent years. A quarter of a century ago, much of the country's corn and soybeans were grown on family-sized farms. But the laws of economics and the development of new crop varieties and gigantic farm machines gave the economic advantage to bigger operations. Little farmers were squeezed out, their land was bought up, and their relatively small farms were combined into big farms. Out came the fences that had separated them and divided their fields. The big planters, chemical fertilizer spreaders, and harvesters began working the longer rows at high speeds. These large farms are your competition if you go into cash grain farming today, and it is a rough way to go indeed on a small holding, when top corn belt land sells for more than $3000 an acre, and farmers pay $60,000 for a new tractor.

One of our neighbors, however, is a city man who bought 150 acres to the west of us and manages to turn a profit on soybeans and corn. But he does not work the farm himself or own a lot of heavy equipment. Instead, he contracts with a neighboring farmer who specializes in share cropping several small farms in the area, thereby farming enough land to justify his own investment in machinery. This is one way a small farm can turn a profit without demanding a heavy investment or even much knowledge of agriculture. It's worth considering provided that: you find the farm you want; it has land suited to crops; and you can find someone to farm it.

If you want to keep livestock and raise enough animals to bring in a profit, take a careful look at any farm you consider in terms of its ability to supply both water and food for the stock. You will need water from a creek, spring, well, or pond that can be piped to troughs or barns. You may also need fields capable of producing hay and grain. Otherwise buying all the necessary feed might make it impossible to earn a profit. Unless you are experienced in raising the kind of stock you have in mind, these early planning stages should include in-depth study about the needs of the animals for pasture, water, and grain, as well as the price of hay you might have to buy during a hard winter. Visit the local county agricultural agent and discuss frankly with him what you have in mind. There could be some local condition that makes it highly risky from the beginning.

Whether you're buying Wyoming ranch land or a piece of Eastern hill country, investigate and understand the mineral ownership and any easements that have been granted.

Whatever your decision, you will probably need more land for a profit-making farm operation than you need if you do not plan to be an active farmer.

Once you decide on the property you would like to buy, you must determine what price to offer the seller. This may be the asking price or it may be less. Up to this point you are not committed to anything. If yours is a reasonable offer that the agent is willing to take to the seller, he will ask you to sign an agreement to buy at the price you are offering. But once you sign the agreement to purchase, you will probably also be asked for a payment of "earnest money," maybe a percentage of the price, as an indication that you are serious about the offer. If the mortgage loan goes through, and the seller accepts your offer, you are obligated to buy or else lose your payment. If the offer is rejected, you recover your earnest money from the realtor.

Bargaining

There is no rule against trying to get the seller to lower his price. Frequently the asking price is well above what he would be willing to accept. The price may have been set high for a variety of reasons. I know one real estate agent who finds new properties simply by driving down country roads and stopping to talk with farmers. The person with whom he talks might not have given the first thought to selling his property. But almost any property has a price beyond which the owner would consider himself a fool to hang onto it.

The agent says, "If somebody came along and offered you $80,000 would you sell?" The owner knows that he wouldn't have much choice, but can't imagine that anybody would pay that kind of money for the "old farm." So he goes along with the idea. The first thing the neighbors know there is a "For Sale" sign in front of his house.

Unless the owner tells the agent not to bring him lower offers, the $80,000 figure may be little more than a starting point. The buyer will not talk money with the seller. Such talk is left to the real estate agent. If the buyer tells the agent he is willing to buy the property for $10,000 less than the asking price, the agent may carry the offer to the seller. The seller can accept or reject the offer. The offer can sometimes be made conditional on the ability of the buyer to borrow the money needed for the purchase.

Usually, as I said earlier, a real estate agent does not like the potential buyers to see the property for the first time unless he is along to show it. But if an agent should give you road directions for finding the property, the best procedure on such visits is not to enter into discussions with the seller, unless you need information that the agent can't supply. If you want to know what price the property sold for the last time it changed hands, you can find the information registered in the court house, accessible to the public, generally in the county recorder's office.

Chances are excellent that the seller is rather proud of the place and the improvements he has made, and there is little for the buyer to gain by talking it down and finding fault. If you want to return for a second or third visit and go over the property more carefully, which is advisable, clear it with the real estate agent who will probably want to mention your visit to the owner first. You will want to inspect back fields to see if there are gullied areas or land that needs expensive work. You will want to check buildings to see if they need repair. Line fences may be important and this is the opportunity to look at them. It is a good idea to see the place on a rainy day. If you like it then, you will still like it when the weather is pleasant. Also you have the opportunity to inspect buildings for leaks, streams for sediment washing in from gullied areas or plowed fields, and to check the condition of farm lanes.

All of this information will help you determine what the property is worth to you, whether or not you want to make an offer, and if so the amount you want to offer.

Usually the seller is responsible for paying for a survey of the land. But if the seller does not want a survey made because of the expense, and insists that the survey is not needed, it may still be a good idea to have it, even if you must pay for it.

Farms are often patched together from pieces of land acquired from different owners at different times. The boundaries may be described in relation to features that have disappeared. Early surveyors often referred to a big oak tree or a rock as the corner of a property, but time takes the big oak tree, and half a century of freezing, thawing, and sedimentation can even cover the rock. The longer it has been since the land was surveyed, the greater the need usually is for a new survey.

In addition, the buyer or the lending agency will want to have a title search made by a title insurance company. The fee for this is normally paid by the buyer. In some places this is a legal requirement. The search should reveal whether or not other people hold any rights to your land or to the water on or around it or to the minerals beneath it. Mineral rights have often been sold separately from surface ownership, and the holder of such rights might be legally entitled to enter your land and drill or strip-mine, even in your front yard. You should also know about easements that might allow other access to your land or provide you a route to get in and get out through the neighbor's place. If you don't have road frontage, you should have an easement.

Among the questions to be answered in your search for a country property, two of the most important are: "How much can I spend?" and "Where will the money come from?" How much you can, or should, invest in farm property is determined by a careful analysis of your total financial picture, including your future income and needs. A conservative approach is preferable. Reach a figure with which you can be comfortable, and then stick to it unless there are special circumstances. Having a figure already in mind when you first go to a real estate agent makes it easier to help your agent locate a suitable property.

Basically, there are two ways to pay for a farm property: 1) in cash at the time of purchase, or 2) in payments spread out over a period of time, perhaps for many years. The easiest way is to pay cash and forget about all the money arrangements and obligations otherwise involved. But few buyers are in a financial position to do that. Even if you are, you might seriously ask yourself if this is a sound policy. Interest payments are currently deductible on your income-tax return. So some buyers try to borrow every dollar they can, leaving their own money to put into their business or investments. Some buyers, convinced that inflation will continue, want to buy at today's prices and pay back with dollars of less actual value in the future. Anyone who has trouble figuring out which is the better course in his own case should consult an attorney or accountant for guidance.

But assuming that you're not going to pay the full amount in cash, you face the question of where to acquire the loan. This is not as simple as walking into the local building-and-loan association and walking out with the money. The city banks you may have dealt with on your home mortgage or business loans will probably not be interested in lending money on property out in the country.

The best place to look for a lending agency is in the area where you are buying. There are several reasons for this. These people know the community, its land values, and farm properties in general. They are interested in the community and in building business there.

Often the real estate agent can be a big help in lining up financing for the farm. He probably knows the local bankers personally, and which ones have money available. One agent I met is not

HOW TO BUY
AND ENJOY
A SMALL FARM

only a major dealer in rural real estate but also is on the board of a local bank.

In making a choice of lending institutions, shop around for the best interest rates available, as you would in dealing with money for any other purpose. For the first time in your experience, you may encounter a strange requirement known as paying "points." This is an extra payment to the bank beyond the legal limit they can charge for interest. Try to deal with a bank that does not charge points. These points are based on the amount of the loan and on a loan of $15,000 may come to $400, payable at the time of the closing on the property.

Most real estate loans involve a mortgage on the property. This is the lending institution's protection against default and enables it to sell the property, in case it must, to regain its investment in it. Payments are generally arranged on a monthly basis, and obviously the shorter the period of the loan, the higher the monthly payments. The fewer the years over which you use the bank's money, the less interest you will pay in the long run for using it. Most institutions can arrange the monthly payments to include a payment on the principal, the interest due, and also insurance and taxes all lumped together.

In determining how much you will be able to repay comfortably every month, keep in mind that you will need money for improvements on the farm, grass, seed, fertilizer, and other expenses and that the biggest expenses may come early in your period of ownership.

You may find that you want to pay off the loan faster than the bank arranged to have it paid. Some banks charge a penalty for this privilege because your early repayment cuts down on the amount of their earnings from interest. Ask whether or not you will be penalized for early repayment and try to borrow the money from a bank that permits you to pay off the debt without penalty if you want to. This stipulation should be written into the loan agreement.

Bankers are not standing at the door with money in their hands. Every loan application is critically studied in relation to the borrower's financial situation and the price and value of the property in question. You will probably be required to submit to the bank a statement of your financial worth, responsibilities, and potential earnings. Your credit rating also becomes a matter of importance. If there are blemishes on it, you may want to explain these to the bank.

Banks are reluctant to lend money on land that has no buildings or other developments on it. This may be a reason, as you search for land, to give extra weight to places that have buildings, even if it has older ones that need repairs.

If the bank informs you that your loan application has been approved, you will go, on a designated day, to meet with the seller, banker, your real estate agent, and perhaps your attorney for what is officially known as the closing. This is the hour when everyone involved gathers around the table and makes the agreement legal, and when you actually become the farm's owner. There will be closing costs in addition to the down payment. The real estate agent will tell you in advance what these will be. You will need a check, perhaps certified, covering the down payment. The "points," if any, must be paid at this time.

In addition, if you have agreed to pay a portion of the surveying costs, or if there is title insurance due, these may be required as part of the closing. All of this may seem confusing for anybody who has not gone through it a time or two, but it's familiar procedure to the banker and the real estate agent. The biggest responsibility you as the buyer have is to bring enough money. It is also highly recommended that your attorney be present.

Another method frequently used to finance land purchase is the land contract. This involves an agreement drawn up by an attorney, arranging that all the conditions of the sale will be between the seller and buyer and will not involve any lending institution. The seller agrees to take his payment in installments over a period of time instead of being paid in a lump sum. He, in effect, replaces the lending institution. Although the buyer moves onto the land and takes immediate possession, as he would with a loan from the bank, he does not get the deed and title until he finishes paying for the property. Meanwhile, he pays off not only the principal but also the interest, which is figured at a rate on which buyer and seller agree. The agreement gives the seller the right to reclaim the property in case the buyer is unable to maintain his regular payments. The seller may be willing to go into this kind of arrangement because of income-tax advantages. And if lending agencies are reluctant to make the loan, the land contract is one more avenue to explore short of giving up. On the other hand, if you are having trouble borrowing money on the property, you may want to take another look at the deal.

CHAPTER

4

SUBSTITUTE HOUSES

Many rural properties advertised have no barn, chicken house, or anything else that might conceivably be converted into a weekend shelter. Even without buildings, there are many reasons you might settle for such open land. It may include a choice building site, a hilltop view, or a small stream twisting along beneath giant shade trees, where you could eventually build a retirement home. Nonetheless there remains the immediate problem of having a place to stay on weekends or on vacations.

The least costly answer is a family-size tent. If you already own a tent, you may use your property as a camp site. Build a low platform to keep the tent off the ground. But a tent is only a warm-season shelter, and it's confining on a rainy day. There is also the question of whether the tent can be left standing from week to week or must be set up with each visit.

Then, there is an immediate need for storage space where you can lock up supplies and hand tools. Lumber yards display tool sheds suitable for lawn mowers and other equipment. Such a shed might even be superior to a tent for those early "camping" visits. Whatever the temporary shelter chosen, it is wise to make yourself as comfortable as possible from the beginning. Discomfort and lack of sanitary facilities may sour family members toward the whole adventure. From the beginning, the farm should be a fun place to visit.

You may want to consider a vehicle that is half-tent, half-trailer. Known as a camping trailer, it is a combination of canvas and aluminum, plastic, or fiberglass. The walls are usually canvas, and they fold down for towing. The big advantages over a tent are that you're up off the ground and the rig has comfortable couches and perhaps a complete kitchen unit, all at a fraction of the cost of a motor home or pick-up coach. Check the want ads for a used trailer. Unless you can park your camping trailer close to a neighbor's barnyard, or otherwise be sure that nobody will bother it, it must be towed back to town after each use.

A minimal cabin may be satisfactory until circumstances permit a better structure. I know one young college executive who longed to have her own place in the country. She searched for months. Then one day her real estate agent showed her an old abandoned farm on the edge of a forest, and it was exactly what she wanted. With the help of friends, she cobbled together a low-cost cabin measuring eight feet by ten feet, providing room enough for a camp stove, table, and bunk beds. The two windows were equipped with wooden shutters that could be locked when the owner was gone. The inexpensive shack tucked away in the edge of the pine woods increased the use the owner could make of the farm.

One of my neighbors bought 60 acres of open hill land several years ago and was confronted with what to do for shelter. He wanted to use the farm and not just spend a few hours there on sunny afternoons. He had an electric line brought in and built a septic tank. Then he bought a motor home. On weekends he loads his family into the motor home, drives out to the farm, parks near his electric and sewer hook-ups and relaxes with all the comforts.

The biggest immediate objection to that arrangement is the high cost of motor homes. Buying the farm is a major expense. For many people, the added cost of a motor home can put the whole plan out of reach. There are on the recreational-vehicle market today a group of "mini-motorhomes," which are about 22 feet long, completely furnished with toilet, refrigerator, stove, beds, and auxiliary power units that operate off either batteries or outside hook-ups. Furthermore these mini-motorhomes have a low depreciation rate. Such a rig could serve for the year or two between the time of buying land and building a summer house or a permanent home.

One Ohio couple bought a 200-acre farm two hours from their city home. They needed a place to stay in the country. If they went to the farm just for the day, they put in four hours of round-trip driving. Instead of a costly motor home, they bought a pick-up truck, and then purchased a camper unit for it. This is still a fairly expensive arrangement, but it does offer versatility. The camper is made to slide into the truck bed where it is clamped down for travel. But the camper unit is equipped with jacks on four corners so it can allow the truck to be driven out from beneath it, a transition usually requiring no more than 10 minutes, and leaving the truck free to haul fence posts or feed for the cattle.

Pick-up coaches are commonly furnished with upholstered seats, table, beds, storage closets, heater, and bath. The kitchen unit can have its own water storage, water heater, propane stove, and refrigerator.

If you don't have a truck or a motor home but still want to get up off the ground, you can choose a travel trailer. These trailers come in a wide variety of designs and sizes. You can park one on your farm and leave it so it need not be towed back and forth each week, although theft or vandalism may make this practice risky in your absence. In time, you can add a wooden deck or patio, outdoor fireplace, and have electricity brought to the trailer. You may want to drill a well and build a septic tank, which could later serve a house if you decide to build.

Wind can damage trailers. With electric wires and gas lines attached, a trailer caught by wind can be highly dangerous. But there is an answer to this problem. You can buy broad metal straps for anchoring trailers against the wind. These are placed over the top of the trailer, attached to metal posts, set in concrete, and screwed down tight. More than one trailer without such protection has blown over in strong winds.

It is not difficult to be comfortable in the country, even in a tent, on a fine, mellow weekend in the spring or autumn. But any temporary shelter has seasonal problems. Winter visits may be next to impossible, and stormy weekends, in any season, limit enjoyment of a country property. If you're prepared for winter, it can be an exciting and interesting season on the farm. To get maximum use out of your country place, you'll want a winterized shelter as soon as possible.

CHAPTER
5
THE OLD FARM HOUSE

When we looked for a farm, we had a good idea of the kind of land we preferred: rolling to rugged topography; woods; and water if possible. But we had no iron-clad rule about the kind of buildings it had to have, or whether it needed buildings at all. Some of the places we considered had buildings; others had none.

Sometimes the property listed has a cabin or hunting lodge. But most often the shelter is an old farm house. Usually an old house, or any kind of house, can add to the seller's asking price. This is fair enough because a shelter adds to the use the new owner will make of a farm. We returned twice to look at one 63-acre offering. There was a fine old beech-maple woods on an interesting hillside. The place had appeal. With a little imagination, we could see a cabin there, a retreat, hidden from the world outside. But this was only in the imagination. In reality, there was no building at all. I was glad later that we passed it up. Now I realize how little we would have used it until we could have invested in some kind of shelter.

The buildings at Spoon Hollow were one of its attractions—the old, open-sided, unpainted tractor shed, the chicken house, a concrete-block structure, and most of all the old farm house that stood on the little slope where it was built of locally grown oak

36

a century ago. The house was not modern, although it had running water from the well and was wired for electricity. It had been occupied until quite recently before we bought it.

A few additions to the farm house soon made it suitable. We put down tile on the kitchen and living room floor. Then we gave the kitchen walls a coat of yellow paint, and Ellen, my wife, hung curtains to match. The sun coming into the room gave it a cheerful glow. There was a single bedroom downstairs, just three rooms in all that were finished. Upstairs, by way of the steepest narrowest stairway I ever saw, was an unfinished attic where farm children no doubt had slept.

As time and funds permit, our plan calls for adding a room downstairs that will extend the kitchen and provide space for a bathroom. The present outdoor facilities are more of a burden on our visitors than they are on us. For us the wonder of having this place in the country is so compelling that we don't feel greatly deprived. For overnight guests from town, the primitive conditions are a test of the bonds of friendship.

People who seek small farms are often looking for features such as those of this hidden valley: creek, woods, and hills. But also watch for drawbacks.

When you first see an old farm house that you like, do not be so smitten by its quaint charm that you overlook its shortcomings. Sooner or later, as new owners, you will come to grips with the question of basic improvements. The better time to think about such matters is before purchasing.

Is the house fit for human occupancy? Can it be made fit at reasonable cost? Will the basic structure someday justify a remodeling job that may turn it into a satisfactory retirement home? Or will you then need to build a completely new house?

There can be sound reasons for considering the renovation of an old farm house. Most of them are of frame construction. As the U. S. Forest Service research people at the Forest Products Laboratory in Madison, Wisconsin have pointed out, "Unlike most material objects, a well-built house, properly maintained does not wear out—at least not over a period of several hundred years. It may become outdated and lack certain conveniences and comforts, but it does not wear out."

I believe our old farm house is as strong today as when it was built one hundred years ago. The oak studs are so hard that termites don't eat them, and driving a nail into them is almost impossible. And there will be no further settling of this structure.

In view of such sturdiness, farm owners should think long and hard before deciding to replace the old house with a new one. If the house is strong, and if it can be renovated to make it suitable for your needs, the least expensive course may be to start working on the old place and give up dreams of building a new one. Besides, there is a saving to society in not using up more wood and other resources than are needed. The basic questions are whether the floors, walls, roof, and foundation are structurally sound. Among the early steps will be to determine whether or not your plans for the house will comply with local codes. Your building contractor and the local officials can give you these answers.

The inspection should begin with the foundation. Even foundation problems, however, if not too extensive, can be corrected. So before giving up the project, get professional advice.

Some old farm houses were not set over basements but were simply constructed on stone foundations with or without a crawl space. You may want to strengthen such a foundation. If the house rests on masonry piers, check these for cracks or uneven settling. Where needed, replace the supports. If your house was set on wood piers, as was common practice in some regions, you may want to replace them with masonry.

The best time to check a basement for water problems, of course, is in wet weather. Spouting problems or improper grading may soak the ground next to the foundation and cause water to come through into the basement. This can usually be corrected. Some poorly-drained locations, however, may have high water tables. In that case, you can't really waterproof the basement.

Fireplaces are attractive, but they can come with built-in troubles and should be inspected to see that they are in order. Friends of ours, searching for a house, always test a fireplace by burning a few sheets of newspaper in it. If it draws well, the paper burns quickly. The fireplace that looks as if it has been used often is probably a satisfactory one. If the fireplace has defects such as cracked or loose masonry, you will want to repair it before putting it to use. The fireplace should have a fireproof lining and the chimney should be inspected to make sure there are no loose bricks.

One farm we considered was advertised as having a "fair house." The floors sloped in many directions, showing there had been serious settling or sagging after it was constructed. This condition might not indicate structural defects, but rather be caused by decay or insect damage. Decay is a special problem where moisture is in contact with wood. A combination of moisture and warm climate creates optimum conditions for decay. Watch for colors that are abnormal in the wood indicating damage of this sort.

Check for insect damage, including termites, carpenter ants, and powder-post beetles. Powder-post beetles, which are most likely to be found in humid conditions near the ground, are recognizable by the holes through which the adults leave, and the sawdust they make. Carpenter ants use the walls as nesting locations and can be detected by the piles of sawdust around their workings. These ants can be destroyed by insecticides. Termites can cause much damage. But they can also be detected and stopped. Termites, in most areas, are the subterranean type. Normally they travel from their homes in the ground to their feeding places in the flooring or walls through mud tubes built up the outer surface of foundations. If you find such tubes, and detect damage, call in a professional to treat them. Then repair the damage the insects have caused.

Roof inspection is an important part of the original check-up. If the roof leaks, the evidence will usually show inside the house as streaks on the walls, spots on ceilings, or discoloring on rafters. Asphalt shingles, which are the most commonly used roofing material, should hold up for about 18 years before the home owner need worry about replacing them. A good wood-shingle roof should last 30 years. Old roofing, chipped and broken along the lower edges, can permit water to get to the wood and cause damage.

When you inspect the flooring, you will want to check for loose or buckled boards as well as places where shrinkage has separated the boards. Before you decide that a floor can be put back in perfect shape by sanding, be certain the sanding operation will not weaken it and endanger its ability to support weight.

Remember also that tile floors showing excessive wear or chipping may have to be completely replaced. They change color with age and you may not be able to match the old tiles with new.

Then take a look at the attic. If it is unfinished, you will be able to see how much insulation it has. If there is none, you should insulate the roof as part of your improvement of the old house. Insulation will cut down heat losses in winter and help keep the house cooler in summer. Other places needing insulation are wall interiors and under the floors where the house has no basement. Compare costs and efficiency of different methods of insulation before making a final choice.

The attic is a good place to start checking out the electrical system. Since the time the old house was first wired, many new electrical gadgets have been invented. Bring in a local electrician at an early date and get his opinion on the condition of the wiring in the house and its ability to carry the load. Both service and safety call for minimizing any delay in rewiring. This step will also give you the opportunity to add outlets and switches for convenience. For example, flood lamps mounted high on the outside corners of the house may be wired so they can be turned on from the bedroom or any other part of the house you wish.

Most old farm houses were designed without benefit of an architect's services. Mom and Dad planned a kitchen and sitting room, counted the kids to figure out how many bedrooms they'd need, and headed for the woods to saw the timbers. A structure built by this method may fall short of modern concepts. But even though the old farm house does not fully measure up, it may have its own charm, and it may have potential if you plan to expand.

In the process of making a final decision, you can assemble some cost estimates of what it would take to put the house in the shape you think it should be. Into this figuring comes considerations of how much of the work, if any, you plan to do, cost of contracted work, and cost of materials needed. People who specialize in rural homes have a rule of thumb for determining how much money should be put into renovation. They say it should not be more than two-thirds the cost of a comparable new home if it is to be economically justifiable.

Owning the old house, instead of a new one, links us to the past and adds a sense of permanence. This was one of our basic reasons for wanting a country place in the beginning. But this intangible has little market value, nor will it keep the rain out. The practical questions must figure heavily into any decision on whether to build or renovate. The final answer depends on both the attitudes of the owners and the condition of the structure.

Adding to the House

Most people setting out to renovate an old farm house find that either it does not have enough space or that the space is not arranged as they would like it. The only answer is to think about enlarging the house or revamping it. In many cases the first necessity will be to install a bathroom. You may need to add a room to a small house, while larger farm houses may have space available in a back porch, closet, or small bedroom. While you're thinking about the plumbing, consider whether you need an additional half-bath. To minimize plumbing costs, you may be able to build the two back-to-back or one above the other on second and first floors.

Finishing upstairs bedrooms may be an inexpensive way to provide space for family or guests, and this project is often the kind that the owner can tackle.

You will also want to plan outdoor living areas, decks and patios. These add to the value, as well as the appeal, of the home and often without high cost. Although you may not plan to add a patio or deck for some months, you can include it in your planning because it may determine the location of additions as well as installation of sliding doors or windows. The changes can then proceed toward a fixed goal as money and time become available.

Partitions can usually be changed, low ceilings can sometimes become cathedral ceilings, decks can be added, stoves or fireplaces can be installed and picture windows built. But the rural home owner who lacks experience and skills in construction should consult first with contractors to determine feasibility and cost.

When You Build a New House

When city people walk over their country property for the first time, they mark in their minds superior sites for a house. What they are looking at in that first appraisal is the general lay of the land and the view they would like from the picture window. But before any final decision is made on the location, other questions should be answered. The house must do more than fit into the landscape and rest on an attractive spot. It has to work. This means giving attention to several specific factors.

The nature of the soil should be suitable for building. There should be gravity flow of effluent possible from house to septic tank and the disposal field below it without endangering the water supply.

Is there a good source of fresh water? Drilling a well may be the first step.

If there is a public water supply, as there is in an increasing number of rural counties, the location of the house in relation to the water main will determine the cost of installing the water line to the house.

Is there enough space for the house and also the other buildings you want to build near it? Barn? Guest house? Garage? What about the garden?

Have you chosen a spot that will avoid problems in building a driveway or farm lane? If the lane would cross low wetlands, climb steep grades, or reach excessive distances from the public road, the costs could become prohibitive. You also want a lane that gives safe access to the public highway.

Check for heavy rocks. If there are large hidden rocks or ledges on the building site, excavation costs can soar.

The topsoil should be suitable for a good lawn, or soil that can be improved for grass. Remember the shade trees. If possible, the house should be located to save them.

Think about the location through all the seasons. What will it be like in winter winds and snowstorms, and during times of heavy rains? It should be on ground above the flood plain, even if the neighbors can't remember ever seeing the creek flood.

Once you have settled these questions and narrowed the selection of building sites, there remains the problem of orienting the building and being certain you have chosen the right direction for the house to face. A careful builder considers the prevailing winds and the location of windows, because these factors will play a role in heating and cooling.

One friend of ours constructed a frame of two-by-fours exactly the size the house foundation would be. He placed this on the spot where the house would go. Then he spent a lot of time there, studying where the sun and wind would hit the house at various times of day and in different seasons, and in general how he and his wife felt about its location. Several times the frame was turned this way or that until finally, both knew they had selected the best possible alignment for the building on their lot. They lived there 18 years and were always glad they took the time and trouble to spot their home carefully.

You seldom find the old farm house just as you have dreamed of it. Circular cherry staircases and summer kitchens were denied the general run of hard-working country families. At the other extreme, and equally appealing to some buyers, are old log cabins, and these are equally hard to find. In our search for a farm property, we saw two or three run-down log cabins. All were looked at longingly, but passed up.

There is a charm in an old log house, but these museum pieces can eat up funds in the remodeling. Most log cabins require extensive and costly repairs. Often there is nothing left but the shell. I saw one ancient weathered structure with 23 acres of rough hill land that had just been sold. The new owner hoped to restore the old house. Pending that time, he had completely covered it with plastic to protect it from further exposure. There she sat, like a Christmas present, probably suffering an accelerated rate of decay beneath the plastic. But the treatment left no doubt about the high value of old houses.

The Fire Hazard

Fire is always a possibility, especially during winter months when a large percentage of home fires occur. The nearest fire department to your farm may be miles away, over roads that are icy or treacherously muddy. The tragic possibility of fire merits thought and various precautions.

First, have an expert check the wiring of the old house, see that it is ample for the load it will carry, and that it meets modern standards. Then check to be certain that you're not tucking electric lamp wires under rugs to get them out of the way. Dust, collecting behind refrigerators and other appliances, can be set afire by a short circuit in an electric wire.

Chimneys are a special threat. Soot building up in a chimney can easily catch fire and burn. This makes an annual cleaning of stove pipe and chimney important.

Check little things that could lead to big fires. Are matches lying around loose instead of stored in glass or metal containers? Do you have careless smokers in the family?

Then ask yourself if you need new fire extinguishers. They should be readily accessible, and everyone should know where they are and how to use them. Smoke detection devices should be installed. If people sleep on the second floor and there is no outside stairway, you should have rope or chain ladders upstairs.

In case of fire, remember that oxygen feeds the fire. Keep burning areas shut away from other parts of the house. And get everyone out before trying to rescue belongings. If the situation is at all hazardous, let the belongings go up in flames.

6

YOUR FARM WATER

SYSTEM

For me there is neither beauty in the old oaken bucket nor virtue in hand pumping water for man or beast. In this age, we have come to expect water to flow, preferably clean and pure, where and when needed, all with minimum expenditure of human energy. Unfortunately, old homesteads may have antique water systems or inadequate sources of clean water. If you plan to keep livestock or irrigate garden or field crops, the water supply becomes even more vital. Hauling water in tank trucks is not a good answer, except in times of emergency.

Water can come either from a surface or underground source. The most common source of farm water, and usually the best, is a well. Wells can be either dug or drilled. Dug wells can give problems. If a dug well is downhill from a pollution source, or if the top of the well is not designed to exclude runoff, it is probably polluted. If all the water getting into the well percolates through enough sand or clay first, it may be safe for drinking. Have your water tested to be sure. If you have an old dug well that gives inadequate or contaminated water, you should consider filling it up and drilling a new well. Deep wells usually yield safe drinking water.

If there were water everywhere under your property, the question of choosing a location for the well would be simple enough. You would select a site away from outhouses, barnyards, feedlots, silos and other sources of contamination but within convenient piping distance. Then call the well-driller. But finding water is almost always tricky and is usually a combination of experience on the part of the driller, and the neighbors, plus the guesswork of the property owner. These, with a dash of luck, can bring a fine producing well.

One of our neighbors built a new house on the ridge and thought he would have no trouble finding water. He called in the driller, picked his spot, and said "there." After 120 feet everyone involved gave up. Dry hole. One problem may have been that the entire ridge is what geologists know as a "karst topography," which means it is underlaid with limestone, and the surface is decorated with sinkholes. But other farms in the area had fair-to-good wells, and our neighbor was determined to do better the next time.

At this point he called in a man he had heard about, a locally noted water dowser, or water witch. The dowser arrived and went about his business with confidence. He cut a forked branch and walked slowly back and forth over the property, holding the stick in front of him with one twig in each closed hand, palms up.

This way of locating water has been used for many decades. Through all that time it has been subject to question and open derision by many, including learned geologists. But what gives country people confidence in dowsing is that often it seems to work. Experienced dowsers say that more of us than we realize possess this inexplicable power to locate water and that experience sharpens the ability.

The dowser finally stopped over a spot where some mysterious force was pulling the forked stick downward toward the ground with a nearly irresistible power.

"Drill here," he advised. "There's a good source of water at 90 feet."

The driller obeyed, and the well provides ample water today. No one can really say whether the driller, without the benefit of that forked stick, would have done better or worse.

Farm planners and agricultural consultants have definite recommendations for anybody planning to hire a contractor to drill a well. First, have a written contract that spells out the per-foot cost of drilling, costs of materials, and costs for any additional services that might be needed such as test-pumping or concrete grouting. Other facts that should be covered in the contract include the size of the well hole, casing specifications, type of seal and grout seal around the casing, test pumping method, completion date, guarantee on materials and work, liability insurance for the driller and the owner, and assurance that the work will conform to state and county regulations.

Once the well is drilled and cased, it should be disinfected to destroy any organisms introduced during the job. This is done by putting a strong chlorine solution into the well casing, running it through the pipe to all faucets, then letting it stand for several hours or overnight. The drilling contractor should handle this treatment as he finishes up the job.

There are some precautions to take in designing the pump house for the well. It should be a buried or insulated chamber separate from the house or other buildings. The electrical wiring to the pump should not go from the house or other farm buildings. If there was a fire, the wiring might be destroyed and the pump would be of no help in supplying water to fight the fire.

Our pump house, which was already in place when we bought the farm, is a small concrete-block structure just large enough to house the pump and its tank. In winter I equip the pump house with two 25-watt light bulbs to burn on very cold nights. I use two in case one burns out. In addition, I pack insulation around the pump, then insulate the structure around the outside with bales of straw to cut out the wind. This system has kept the water in the pump house from freezing even when temperatures fell to minus 25° F. The lights must be turned on and off by either a timer or the human hand. During the coldest weather, you may need heat in the pump house around the clock. A sunken pump house will cut down the need for such auxiliary heating, but it requires excavation.

The cleaner the water and the more abundant the supply, the less trouble you'll have with the pump.

Let Gravity Work

Our old farm house is on a hillside, downhill from Pine Pond which covers a fourth of an acre. This is an excellent arrangement for more than one reason. Although I can take no credit for building the pond uphill from the house, I approve of it highly and would recommend it to anyone building a small pond who has the topography for such an arrangement.

Pine Pond is eight feet at its deepest and no more than 200 feet across in any direction. It is held in place by an excellent grass-covered dam. The grove of native pines that give it its name rims most of it. The topography carries excess pond water safely past house and yard. Not only is it beautiful, but I am fond of it for more practical reasons as well.

When Pine Pond was constructed, a concrete filter was installed in its deepest part, and out of this runs a pipe two inches in diameter that extends beneath the dam to a control valve, housed in a sunken tank well below the frost line. The housing for this valve is a 20-inch-diameter ceramic tile buried vertically in the lower outside edge of the dam. Extending through the downhill side of the tank is a short-threaded pipe, permitting us to attach hoses and to drain the pond if we should ever want to.

The site we chose for our garden is 300 feet from Pine Pond and 20 feet lower. This arrangement made it convenient to run a waterline from the valve at the pond to the garden. Three-quarter-inch plastic pipe cost me $14 per 100 feet. I also needed 50 feet of soaker-type garden hose with holes along one side, some plastic connectors and clamps for the pipe, and a shutoff valve to put on the line at the garden for convenience. When this system was hooked up (the job required perhaps an hour), it delivered irrigation water under good pressure to the garden whenever I turned on the valve. Besides, there was no pump or electric motor using energy and making noise. The irrigation system played a major role in the production of tomatoes, beans, potatoes, strawberries, and sweet corn that first year. Total cost, aside from the labor, was under $50.

We also learned that water held in that 300 feet of black hose would become hot to the touch on sunny days. This first water from the hose was too hot for the growing plants, but it gives us enough hot water for an outdoor shower. We rigged up a simple framework and enclosed it with a shower curtain, then installed a slatted floor. By attaching a nozzle to the garden hose and hanging it over the framework, we had a hot shower anytime we left water standing in the hose for 30 minutes or more in the sun.

There is one other refinement in our gravity-flow water system. Where the line passes the house, halfway between Pine Pond and the garden, it is equipped with a valve where we can take off pond water for shrubs, fruit trees, the rhubarb bed, squash, and flowers planted close to the house.

When winter comes, we shut the water off at the pond and drain the hoses carefully.

If your old farm has no indoor plumbing, you can use a long section of black garden hose to absorb the sun's heat and provide enough hot water for a summer-afternoon shower.

Pond Water for Drinking

A pond can also be the source of drinking water. If the pond can be located near the buildings, without danger from pollution, this will mean lower costs for pipe and electrical wiring. The pond should be 10 feet deep or deeper, with depths of 3 feet or more around the edges to keep vegetation from emerging. The dam should be equipped with a pipe so the pond can be drained. The nature of the land that serves as the watershed is important because your drinking water must wash across this land. The best watershed is a good cover of grass or a wooded area to help keep silt out of the pond. Silt will shorten both the life of the pond and the efficiency of the filtering system. Livestock can contaminate the pond and destroy cover around it, so domestic animals should be fenced out.

Treatment of pond water is generally done in three stages, beginning with a settling basin to clear the water of suspended particles. Then the water goes through a filtration treatment where sand traps any floating materials not cleared out during the settling process. There still remains the need to kill harmful bacteria in the water because filtration and sedimentation will not totally purify the water. Purification is usually accomplished with a chlorinating system. There are test kits available to check such a home water source to be certain that the treatment is effective. The county health department can offer guidance in making these tests.

A pond water system will require a storage reservoir capable of holding enough water to keep the farm going for a couple of days or more. The filtering process takes time and you may need treated water faster than the system will supply it. Farm research specialists at the University of Kentucky say you will need 50 gallons per day per person, 10 gallons per steer, 4 per hog and 3 per sheep, plus 5 gallons for each 100 chickens.

Facts about Cisterns

I am prejudiced against cisterns, probably because I have been exposed to low-quality water from them. But the cistern can hold good supplies of soft water for washing, and in some places it may be the only practical source of drinking water. With modern technology, cistern water can be free of dirt and soot.

The cistern must be planned correctly from the beginning. Too many cisterns in times past were not equipped to keep out the first water from a rain. This early part of the rainfall washes the roof free of soot, assorted particulates, and bird droppings. These foreign materials can be directed away from the cistern so that the water saved comes from a clean, washed roof. Roof washers may be either home made or one of the commercial types available at building supply stores. Such a washer can be made from a barrel or tank with a capacity equal to 10 gallons for each 1,000 square feet of roof area. The tank has an overflow built into a trough that sits on top of the barrel. The device is screened and water from the downspout flows into the trough and drops through a four-inch-wide slot into the barrel until the barrel is filled. As the rain continues, the water overflows through a four-inch pipe into the cistern. The barrel should have an outlet, with a faucet, at the bottom to empty the water. You can use this water for the flower garden or livestock.

Some cistern owners also want the collected water to go through a sand filter before entering the cistern. Provided the filter is kept clean, it can help improve water quality. In a heavy rain, however, the filter may work so slowly that some water will be sent through the overflow and wasted. If you plan to use the cistern only for livestock water or irrigation, this filtering is not necessary.

If your farm comes complete with an old cistern, it may need repairing or even replacing. Inside walls can be replastered. It should be thoroughly inspected to see what needs to be done to make it into a safe water system. But drinking water from the cistern, even though sand-filtered, will probably need to be chlorine-treated. There are commercial suppliers who offer equipment for this. An activated carbon or charcoal filtering system can also help remove odors and tastes.

If you want to know the capacity of an old cistern, measure the length and width to get the area in square feet and then multiply this by the depth in feet. The resulting figure multiplied by $2\frac{1}{2}$ will give you the number of gallons the cistern will hold.

Testing the Water

The fact that former owners drank the water does not guarantee safety for those unaccustomed to it. The best plan, after acquiring a new country property, is to get the water tested at once.

In our area, all we had to do was call the county health department. Two days later, an employee carrying little sterile bottles arrived at the farm. Perhaps the most critical step in testing water is taking the sample. If the laboratory testing the water in your area permits owners to take the sample, be sure to follow instructions carefully. Nothing, except the water being tested, should ever touch the inside of the bottle or its cap. First, make sure the outside of the faucet furnishing the sample is clean and dry. Then, after letting the water run full force for a minute or more, draw the sample while being certain that water going into the jar does not touch any objects or hands on its way. Cap the bottle at once, and deliver it to the laboratory within a few hours if possible.

CHAPTER

7

SANITATION SYSTEMS

City people turning to the land for the first time may think privies were invented by cartoonists. For these people, who are accustomed to swirling waters that quickly flush all waste from sight, the presence of an outhouse comes as a cultural shock. But a current school of thought could, in the years ahead, lead us away from our dependence on flush toilets. In some regions, water shortages will encourage use of alternatives. Forty percent of the household water used in this nation gets flushed down toilets. A single push on the lever sends five gallons or more down the drain, and usually this is from a high-quality source and fit for human consumption.

Those seeking alternatives to the flush toilet are considering the compost toilet. Perhaps the best known of these is the Clivus Multrum, designed in Sweden where it is widely used. It uses no chemicals or water, and it has already been approved by the health departments of some states. It can be built either inside or outside. The principle on which it works is to decompose waste materials through bacterial action in the presence of oxygen. This chemical reaction releases only carbon dioxide and water vapor and leaves a small residue of clean humus that can be removed from a separate chamber every year or two and spread on the flower bed. Odors are said to be minimal and not noticeable, except on rare occasions when a down-draft forces the air back down the ventilator pipe. A fan solves this problem.

A number of such toilets are available, including the American-made Ecolet. Some home owners have built their own compost toilets. The Clivus Multrum, which seems to be the most costly, carries a price tag of around $1,800. What you buy is a large fiberglass container, eight feet long, five feet high, and shaped like a boot. It has separate compartments for toilet wastes and kitchen wastes, and another for a storage chamber. The floor of the container slopes at a 30 degree angle so materials gradually move down as they are decomposed. A major appeal of the composting toilet, aside from its using no water, is that it is a non-polluting system. No need to worry about the location in relation to the sources of drinking water or other water.

Where there is no sewer line, septic tanks are still the standard accepted structure throughout rural areas. Some of these systems work better than others. The design is a concrete or plastic tank (these can be purchased commercially) with two compartments divided by a wall that does not reach the top. The tank is buried. Lines from the house carry waste materials into the first chamber, where solids settle to the bottom allowing liquids to cross the divider into the second chamber. From there they flow through a line, usually plastic, and are directed into drain lines that extend out from the septic tank through leeching beds of crushed stone. The whole thing is neatly covered and hidden from sight. These systems work less well in heavy clay soils, where water does not soak into the ground readily. Bacterial action breaks down the solid wastes, and for this reason detergents (which kill bacteria) can be bad for the system and should be kept out of it.

The design of septic tanks is carefully controlled by local health departments. The amount of leach lines and other features of the system are established to meet local conditions, and to fit the soil type and number of people the system is supposed to serve. Step one, if you must install a septic tank, is to call your local health department for these basic guidelines. Penalties aside, the reason for compliance to the rules is to protect streams and ground water from contamination.

There remain, however, farms where the old privy is still in use. If you should need to move or build one, there are some guidelines to bear in mind for maximum sanitation.

Location should be the prime consideration. You do not want to contaminate water sources. The privy should sit downhill from well or spring and a hundred feet from such a water source.

Make the pit big enough to serve for six years or more. Six feet deep for a pit four feet square should guarantee long life for the privy.

To keep out rodents and insects, set the building on a concrete sill, built all around the perimeter of the pit. This will also keep rain water out of the pit and give the structure a firm level footing. The floor and seat should also be sealed tightly. Then screen all openings. Keeping the pit dark will help discourage flies. There should be a vent pipe from the pit extending two feet above the roof to minimize odors. Ashes from the wood-burning stove, or an occasional sprinkling of lime, will also help control odors.

Before the pit is full, dig a new one, move the structure to it, and fill in the old pit.

CHAPTER

8

WOOD FIRES AND TAPPING THE SUN

Farm buyers usually want a woodburning fireplace until the first bitterly cold morning when they find that open fireplaces can be highly impractical providers of warmth. Where I grew up, we burned coal because this was our most convenient fuel. Whatever the fuel, much of the heat is smoothly drawn up the fireplace chimney into the big outdoors. Warming yourself on a cold morning was a matter of elbowing your way into the line of people standing as close as possible to the fire while turning slowly in a futile effort to warm all sides. For this reason, many fireplaces, built to heat homes, have been sealed with brick and plaster. A far better way (where heat, not charm, is the goal) is a wood-burning stove.

Such a stove is most commonly a plain metal fire box into which you feed sticks of wood as needed. Although this is a step up from the open fireplace, it too can be highly inefficient. The fire tends to burn faster as its heat increases, until the fuel is consumed.

For greatest efficiency, you need a stove with an airtight fire box and a way to control oxygen fed to the fire. Many stoves on today's market will do. Wood-burning stoves have found new popularity in recent years with the rising cost of fossil fuels.

The stove we chose for the old farm house at Spoon Hollow lacks the esthetic appeal of an open fireplace. Although its flame is not open to view, the house stays uniformly warm. Ours is what is known as the Ashley-type stove and comes with a bimetalic coil-type thermostat, which expands as the fire becomes hotter and contracts as the firebox cools. This contracting and expanding action lifts or lowers a chain attached to an air intake door, permitting more or less oxygen to enter the fire box.

Wood does not have to be split for this stove. It can be fed into the fire box in 22-inch-long logs eight or ten inches in diameter. The complete log will burn. Our fire does not have to be banked for the night by covering it with ashes to slow down the rate of burn. On a winter night before retiring, I fill the stove with large pieces of wood and set the draft low. Fired in this way, the stove maintains an even heat all night. I've had a stovefull of oak hold a fire for 12 hours, but 8 hours is average. In the morning, we need only open the draft and add more fuel.

Wood becomes a more efficient fuel as it becomes hotter. As it approaches temperatures of about 1100° F, the heat drives off volatile gases and liquids. These will also burn, providing addi-

This modern wood-burning stove may lack the charm of a fireplace, but its thermostatic control enables the fire to keep going all night.

tional heat. The burning gases can account for as much as 60 percent of the heat available in wood. This is part of the process of turning the wood into charcoal. Less effective modern stoves produce the charcoal but do not burn the gases.

It has long been the dream of manufacturers of wood-burning stoves to create one that reaches maximum efficiency, burning both gases and the charcoal completely. A secondary reason for designing such a stove is to burn the volatile gases and liquids that might otherwise accumulate on flue walls, setting the stage for a chimney fire. Some manufacturers attempt to get complete combustion by providing for secondary sources of air to the firebox. But this air must be warmed, or else it cools the volatile gases below the point where they will burn. Achieving maximum efficiency is a difficult problem and one that has not been solved completely.

The best procedure in picking out the right stove is to survey the market carefully, read the literature, compare the claims of the manufacturers and the designs of their stoves, and, whenever possible, talk with people who are using wood-burning stoves.

If you prefer central heating, consider the wood-burning furnaces on the market. Such furnaces can be installed without air ducts. Instead, heat from the furnace can rise through registers in the floor, warming the room above.

A wood-burning furnace may put more stress on an old chimney than a gas or oil furnace, so when you install the system, it's wise to have a local mason check the chimney and make sure it can handle the job.

There is no doubt that gas or oil heat is simpler and easier to use, and less trouble than burning wood as a fuel. Wood has to be cut, the stove fired, and the ashes removed. Although it takes more labor, wood, when properly burned, is a highly efficient fuel. For the farm owner with his own supply of wood, it's a most satisfying source of heat.

Wood-burning furnaces can also be combined with oil burners that kick in automatically when no one is home or the supply of wood runs out.

For anyone interested in wood-burning furnaces, here are a few names of manufacturers:

Riteway, Division of Sarco Corp., P. O. Box 6
   Harrisonburg, Virginia 22801
Longwood Furnace Company, Gallatin, Missouri 64640
Sam Daniels Company, Box 868
   Montpelier, Vermont 05602

Even people who must buy fire wood by the cord may find it cheaper for heating than gas, coal, or electricity. There's also the satisfaction of knowing you're on the right side of the environmental issue. Someday the petroleum products are going to run out, but properly managed forests renew themselves. Besides, wood fire pollutes the air less than petroleum products do.

The kinds of wood you have on your farm will help determine how efficient your wood-burning system can be. Hard woods provide more heat per unit than soft woods. The table on pp. 60–61 ranks various common firewoods for their heating efficiency.

RATING FOR FIREWOOD

HARDWOODS

	Relative Heat	Easy to Burn	Easy to Split	Heavy Smoke	Throws Sparks
EXCELLENT					
ash	High	Yes	Yes	No	No
beech	High	Yes	Yes	No	No
birch	High	Yes	Yes	No	No
dogwood	High	Yes	Yes	No	No
hard maple	High	Yes	Yes	No	No
hickory	High	Yes	Yes	No	No
pecan	High	Yes	Yes	No	No
red oak	High	Yes	Yes	No	No
white oak	High	Yes	Yes	No	No
GOOD					
cherry	Medium	Yes	Yes	No	No
soft maple	Medium	Yes	Yes	No	No
walnut	Medium	Yes	Yes	No	No
FAIR					
aspen	Low	Yes	Yes	Medium	No
basswood	Low	Yes	Yes	Medium	No
cottonwood	Low	Yes	Yes	Medium	No
elm	Medium	Medium	No	Medium	No
gum	Medium	Medium	No	Medium	No
sycamore	Medium	Medium	No	Medium	No
yellow-poplar	Low	Yes	Yes	Medium	No

SOFTWOODS

	Relative Heat	Easy to Burn	Easy to Split	Heavy Smoke	Throws Sparks
GOOD					
Douglas-fir	High	Yes	Yes	Yes	No
eastern red cedar	Medium	Yes	Yes	Medium	Yes
southern yellow pine	High	Yes	Yes	Yes	No
western red cedar	Medium	Yes	Yes	Medium	Yes
white-cedar	Medium	Yes	Yes	Medium	Yes
FAIR					
cypress	Medium	Medium	Yes	Medium	No
eastern white pine	Low	Medium	Yes	Medium	No
larch	Medium	Yes	Yes	Medium	Yes
ponderosa pine	Low	Medium	Yes	Medium	No
redwood	Medium	Medium	Yes	Medium	No
sugar pine	Low	Medium	Yes	Medium	No
Tamarack	Medium	Yes	Yes	Medium	Yes
true firs	Low	Medium	Yes	Medium	No
western white pine	Low	Medium	Yes	Medium	No
POOR					
spruce	Low	Yes	Yes	Medium	Yes

U. S. Department of Agriculture
Forest Service Leaflet No. 559

Although some modern wood-burning stoves will burn green wood, the yield of heat increases as the wood dries out. According to the U. S. Forest Service, drying of a log increases the heat it will provide by as much as 44 percent. The firewood should be stacked near (but not against) the house months ahead of winter's first snow.

Solar Energy

One afternoon while driving through the northern part of our county, I passed Hartzell Wallingford's place and noticed a strange pattern of black hose looped along the roof of his garage.

Wallingford, who is known locally as a man of inventive and imaginative ideas, likes country living. He also likes the feeling of self-sufficiency that comes from sawing his own firewood and putting the products of his land to work supplying the family needs. I wanted to see what he was doing with all that hose making regular patterns against the aluminum-painted surface of his garage roof.

What he was doing was exactly what an increasing number of people are doing in these times of high energy prices and threatened resources: he was working out his own low-cost method of heating water, as well as his house. He gave me a guided tour that was an eye-opener.

First he showed me his inexpensive water-heating system. He had bought 200 feet of black plastic hose at a total cost of about $26. He ran the hose up and down both sides of the metal roof of his garage. Well water that was going into his basement water heater was detoured through the rooftop hose first. He soon found that on sunny days water flowing into the tube was quickly heated. This system would provide him with 15 gallons of hot water almost anytime he wanted it.

Wallingford also installed a wood-burning stove in his basement. He cuts enough wood to keep the stove burning through the winter. The small stove keeps the entire house heated comfortably. In addition, it serves as another water heater in cloudy weather. Wallingford had attached copper tubing to the jacket of the wood burner. By feeding water through it and back into the water heater, he keeps a hot-water supply ample for family needs. In emergencies, he can still turn to electrically heated water.

All parts of this system are arranged to blend together for the best combination of saving energy. Because of his wood stove, his fuel-oil furnace became a supplemental heater for the house instead of the prime source of heat.

"Last winter," Wallingford told me, "I burned about 15 gallons of fuel oil. That's all."

Similar work has been done by dozens of other private individuals determined to cut down on their dependence on public utility companies and reduce their energy costs. Architects, builders, planners, and scientists are deeply interested in the

A low-cost way to absorb the sun's energy for heating water is to run loops of black plastic hose up and down a roof, as this man has done.

potential for solar energy. This attitude makes sense. Solar energy is clean, abundant, and versatile. The sun is the greatest storehouse of energy available to the world today. According to Donald A. Beattie of the U.S. Energy Research and Development Administration, if we were to total all the energy locked in the earth's remaining stores of coal, oil, and natural gas, it would be only one-twenty-fifth of the energy available from the sun in a single year. The tapping of this energy does not always call for costly, sophisticated equipment, as Hartzell Wallingford and many others have proven. Solar energy is becoming increasingly competitive with fossil fuels, and there is much you can do to put the sun to work if you are planning to build or remodel your farm dwelling.

CHAPTER

9

LANES, FENCES, AND POLE BARNS

Once, as a young farm reporter, I drove up a long twisting gravel lane leading to the hilltop home of an Indiana hog farmer. The man's name has escaped me, but his words remain. My assignment was to write an article telling how to keep a farm lane in good condition. When I put the question to the farmer, his answer was brief: "Never drive in the same rut twice."

Quality advice drawn from experience should always be taken seriously. But there may be a few additional pointers that will help owners of farm lanes plagued by the never-ending task of keeping the driveway in shape. Much of the problem with a farm lane may come from its original location. But there may be little we can do about this on old farms where decades of travel by assorted vehicles has carved the lane into the landscape.

Our own lane, leading down off the public road along the ridgetop into our hollow, gives us frequent problems. It is covered with crushed limestone trucked in from a quarry 14 miles away. Vehicles tend to push rock and gravel deeper and deeper into the ground during the wet seasons. There seems no limit to how many tons can be pounded into the earth along that narrow strip.

My road-maintenance technique revolves around an effort to

keep water off the lane as much as possible. Instead of letting rain run down the tracks or the center of the road, I took early steps to direct it off the road into ditches along the sides. This was not difficult. My engineering tool was a long-handled shovel judiciously employed during a heavy rain, when you don't need surveying instruments to reveal where the water will run. I made a series of little wing-dam ditches that direct the water off the road into the ditches on both sides. These are not difficult to maintain. But they are not always easy to drive over. They do tend to discourage speeding, which also destroys country lanes.

The long-handled shovel is a good tool for directing water off a country lane to keep it solid and protect it from erosion.

A road serviceable the year around is vital. Without it, there may be weeks when you can't visit the farm. If you have a tractor equipped with a blade, you can manage much of your own road maintenance. You can keep the ditches open and the stone or gravel scraped into the tracks where it will do the most good.

Generally, what needs to be done is to study the road, preferably during a heavy rainstorm. Watch where the water runs, see if it could be redirected (often with minimum labor), and thereby prevent gullies and the loss of gravel.

Lanes that are nearly impassible or that are so poorly designed that each storm destroys them may need major redesigning and contract work. Some may have to be replaced.

Farm Fences

Chances are excellent that when you buy your old farm you will find fences where you do not want them and need fences where you do not have them. Putting up fences can be costly. But some fence building may be essential if you or your neighbors have livestock.

Farmers' fences have taken many forms depending on materials available. Oldtimers can remember rock fences, stump fences, and rail fences, which have given way to more modern designs, including wire and, on some horse farms, board fences. Most of us want a fence that's strong enough to hold back the animals, long-lasting, and not so unsightly that it detracts from the pleasant appearance of the rural landscape or the value of the farm.

Some regions of the country have fence designs that have become almost standard. In parts of the west, fields are fenced with sheep-tight and predator-proof structures consisting of 36-inch woven or net wire with the lower six inches folded under, buried and weighted down with rocks. Above this wire are two or three strands of tightly stretched barbed wire. Unfortunately, this fence design has proved a real barrier to wildlife, especially the pronghorn antelope, which needs freedom to roam. Ranchers who want to allow the passage of antelope know that the bottom wire needs to be 16 inches above the ground because these swift-footed range runners do not leap over fences, as do deer, but instead get down and belly under them. Sometimes antelope hit a fence full tilt and hang up and die. Wherever you buy your farm take note of local fencing designs and consider the merits.

You need to determine whether or not local or state regulations govern the legal fence between properties or along highways. In some, but not many, places you may even need a fencing permit.

The most common kind of fencing is made of barbed wire stretched between wood or steel posts set at intervals of 16 to 20 feet. The easiest to handle are steel posts because they can be driven instead of being set in dug or drilled holes. These posts are lightweight and easily driven in. Usually they will outlast wood posts. In addition, unless used in very dry soil, steel posts provide a ground to protect fences against lightning. They should be good for 15 years or more.

These posts are available in farm supply stores and are sold in a variety of lengths ranging from five to eight feet. There are special steel posts sold for corners, where there is greater strain on the post.

The posts can also be provided with steel anchor plates which are either riveted, bolted, or clamped in place so they are underground once the post is driven. Anchor plates give added support against rubbing and pushing by livestock.

Wood posts may be bought from neighboring farmers or a farm-supply store or cut from your own woodlot. But if you set out to harvest your own fence posts, bear in mind that you will build a longer-lasting fence if the posts are made largely of heart wood. Posts set in the ground with the bark intact may last no more than two or three years, because they become feeding stations for fungi. Most fenceposts first rot and break near or below ground level, where moisture and oxygen are available for fungi. But there are steps you can take to delay this decay and lengthen the life of the fence strung on wooden posts.

First is the choice of wood. Our choice back where my father taught me fence building was black locust, which is an extremely tough wood. It was also abundant then. Red cedar ranks right along with black locust for durability. The only wood superior is osage orange, known by some people as hedge apple. If you remove the bark and most of the sapwood from wood posts, and do not give them any special treatment, osage orange should last a quarter century or more, while black locust and red cedar will hold up 15 to 25 years. Sassafras should last 10 to 15 years. Among those good for 5 to 10 years are white oak, blackjack oak, and cypress. Hickory, pine, sweetgum, red oak, sycamore, cottonwood, willow, and yellow poplar may do the job for two to seven years.

Posts can be treated with preservative to give them added life. This treatment can be done either commercially or by the farmer. Commercially treated fence posts usually last longer than those home-treated. Commercial treatment forces the preservative deeper into the wood under pressure, while home treatment penetrates only to the depth the wood will soak up from being submerged in the liquid.

Posts to be home-treated with preservative should have the bark removed but the sapwood left. The sapwood can absorb the preservative well. The best season for removing bark is spring and early summer. A drawknife or other sharp heavy tool will strip it from the posts. Then the posts should be thoroughly dried by stacking them with ample space between them for air circulation.

Pentachlorophenol ("Penta") is the most widely used wood preservative for the home treatment of fence posts. This oil-soluble preservative is both effective and relatively inexpensive. It is also easy to use. Generally it is sold under a variety of trade names, in concentrated liquid form. This concentrate is then mixed with a petroleum solvent, such as diesel oil, to make a five percent solution. If you buy the 10 to 1 Penta concentrate, it will need to be mixed at a ratio of one gallon of concentrate to 10 gallons of oil.

This liquid can be used in 55-gallon oil drums that have had one end removed. The safest procedure is to set the drum in a hole about half its depth so it will not tip over. Some farmers make horizontal tanks by cutting drums vertically through their center then welding them together on the open ends, providing an area in which the posts can be submerged in the preservative.

When using the upright drum, set the posts in enough preservative to cover the lower half and leave them there for at least 48 hours. You may want to treat them for up to 72 hours, although the top may need less treatment than the bottom. The drum should be covered to keep out rain water.

Wear clothes that will protect you. If the preservative splashes onto your skin, wash it off as quickly as you can. Generally, livestock will not be harmed by touching treated posts.

Where the fence needs extra strength on corners and at gates, you may want to use concrete posts cast in place. These may well outlast the builder if they are well built.

Barbed wire long ago became the standard building material for fencing, especially for cattle pastures. Some western rangeland is fenced with as little as two strands of barbed wire, although four or five strand fences are more common. Good fences are often combinations of woven wire topped with a strand or two of barbed wire.

For some purposes, woven wire is a necessity. Farmers raising sheep and hogs can't rely on barbed wire alone. Hogs may need a strand of barbed wire at the bottom of a woven wire fence to keep them from rooting out and escaping. Livestock farmers sometimes expect fences to keep predators away from sheep, hogs, and calves. Usually the worst predators are free-roaming dogs, and it takes a tight fence to turn them. Whatever the fence design chosen, it should be matched to the possible uses of the field, now and for the coming years. The high cost of fencing is one reason for long-range planning.

The easiest fences to build are those that stand in long straight lines across level ground. Curving fences, such as those you might need for contour farming, are not as strong as straight fences because there are greater pressures on the line posts.

Deep gullies can be especially difficult to build fence across. The best plan is often to build straight across the gully and then add fencing below so livestock cannot walk up the gully and out of the field. On a very deep gully, you may be able to end the fence on both sides easier than you can build down into the ditch. Use strong anchor posts on either side of the gully. Turn to this plan only where the terrain will guarantee that livestock will not escape.

If you're building a fence along a new course, it is not difficult to lay out a straight line, provided the ground is level. The trick is first to set a post at each end of the fence line. Then, with a helper, set stakes at 100-foot intervals between the two end stakes.

Have your helper sight down the line from one end to be certain each stake you drive is kept in line with the end posts.

The job is more difficult where the fence line goes over a hill and drops from sight. At the crest of the hill, set *two* poles or stakes where you think they're in line with the end poles. Then, with a helper, move these hilltop stakes until they line up with the end poles. Next, drive stakes along the line between the hilltop and each end.

The fence line, once established, may need to be cleared before the fence building can proceed. Trees, stumps, brush, and old wire from earlier fences may block your way. If you have a tractor equipped with a blade, or a bulldozer, this is the time to put the machine to work. In a single pass you may be able to clear a path for the new fence. A heavy disk harrow can be used to work down the smaller brush once you have cleared the line of larger trees and obstructions. This working of the soil also helps prepare the ground for the growth of a linear wildlife refuge once the fence is completed.

If you do not have heavy equipment to clear the fence line, you may have to turn to brush axe and mattocks. These tools have not been improved substantially in the last half century and are great consumers of human energy. This rugged work, taken in moderation by the physically able, has some appeal. Land clearing can be less boring than jogging.

After clearing away the debris, you will want to mark with shovel, mattock, or driven stake the location for each fence post, taking care to keep them all in line. When the ground is moist, metal posts can be pounded in. One tool used for this is a pipe large enough in diameter to fit over the top of the post. The end of this pipe is welded shut. The pipe, when moved up and down over the post, becomes a pile-driver.

Wooden posts can also be driven if they are sharpened on one end. New England farmers, driving red cedar posts, use a heavy wood maul for this job. You can either have a helper hold the post in position for those first taps that set the point, or you can shape a starting hole with a pointed iron rod by driving it into the ground a foot or so and moving it around to form a cone-shaped hole.

Our system, where I grew up, was to use a post-hole digger.

That consists of a pair of twin curved blades, hinged together, with two long handles. The technique is to stab the earth with this instrument with such force that the blades cut several inches deep, then pinch the blades together by spreading the handles and neatly lifting a circular plug of earth from the hole. That, at least, is the idea. In practice, it is not accomplished so neatly. The blades are deflected by stones and the roots of oak trees, while stone-hard earth yields only chips. Part of the misery of this procedure has been overcome by the invention of post-hole augers that attach to the power-take-off on a farm tractor and worm their way into the earth in a hurry. There are also hand augers that can substitute for the post-hole digger.

When the hole is dug, drop the wooden fence post into it and shovel the loose earth back around the post. Tamping the earth solidly enough to keep the post from wobbling is the real difficulty in this system.

Driven posts are more solidly set than posts set in dug or drilled holes because the earth around them remains tightly packed and hard. Line posts should be set 1½ to 2 feet deep if they are steel, and 2 to 2½ feet deep if they are wood.

Corner posts are a special problem because of the added stress they must take. The distance between line posts should be shortened for added strength as the fence nears a corner post. The wood post for a fence corner should be 5 to 6 inches in diameter, and set at least 3½ feet in the ground. Corner posts should also be braced with diagonal braces or wires anchored to brace posts. You can set corner posts in concrete for still greater strength.

Wire, whether woven or barbed, must be stretched and held in place until it can be fastened to the poles. Woven wire, which usually sells in 330 foot rolls, should be stretched from one anchor post, such as a corner post, to the next. If the anchor posts are set in concrete, be sure you do not stretch the fence between them until the concrete has had plenty of time to harden thoroughly. If you are going to top the fence with barbed wire, put on the woven wire first. Where livestock is likely to rub against the wire, put the wire on the side of the posts next to the pasture. But if appearance is the main object, attach the fence to the "outside" of the posts.

Start by unrolling the woven wire the length of a couple of

line posts and standing it on end. Then wrap the ends of the wire around the first anchor post and splice the ends back to the woven wire. Determine the proper height for the wire, and then staple it in position to the anchor post. Next, unroll it to the next anchor post. Gradually pull it fairly tight, using a fence stretcher, tractor, or block and tackle. Fencing should be tight but not so tight that it might break and wrap around whoever gets caught in the way. Then begin fastening it to the line posts, working from the top down on each post. Use staples on wood posts and wire clamps on steel posts.

Electric Fences

An electrically charged wire can be added to an old fence to turn livestock. This is one way the electric fence can be of service. The advantages of this type of fence are the low cost and the ease of moving it. The shock administered by these fences is harmless enough, but it packs enough authority to make livestock respect it. Instead of being a continuous flow, electricity usually charges through the line in one tenth of a second bursts as many as 5 times a minute. These electrically charged wires must be insulated from the posts that support them and not be grounded by plants or other objects. Although electric fencing can be used for sheep and hogs, it is more commonly used for cattle and horses. It is also used to keep wildlife out of gardens and flower beds. Check with your equipment dealer or county agent to see if there are any local or state regulations governing the use of electric fences.

Gateways

The simplest kind of gate is made of three strands of barbed wire fastened to poles that serve as spreaders to keep the strands separated. One end of this rig is fastened permanently to one gatepost; the other end can be unfastened to open the gate. A loop of baling wire holds the lower end of the movable pole in place while another loop slips down over the top of the pole. In some places this is known as a Texas gate, or western gate. Its simplicity of construction and low cost are its only known virtues.

Most farmers use Texas gates only between pastures. Around the home, barnyard, and entrance to the farm, you can use many more esthetically pleasing designs. Farm-equipment dealers sell aluminum gates that swing freely and last a long time. One of our early tasks at Spoon Hollow was to install a gate at the entrance to the farm lane, which leads off the public road. I bought two six-by-six pressure-treated yellow-pine posts and set them in concrete three feet deep. The post that supports the weight of the gate was set first. I had already drilled holes for the bolts to hold the gate. After the concrete was hard and the post would not move in any direction, we hung the gate on it. The end of the bottom bolt was turned up to support the lower metal loop on the end of the gate, and the matching bolt at the top was turned down to engage the upper loops on the gate. So the two bolts tended to lock the gate in place, making it difficult for thieves to lift it off. Then we placed the second gatepost and, before the concrete around its base was hard, maneuvered it carefully into the exact position that allowed the gate to swing freely so a latch would fit. We then left the gate open until the second post was solid in its setting.

Usually a gate post must support a considerable amount of weight, so the post—after application of a preservative—should be set in concrete.

Cattle guards are a popular substitute for gates because they can be crossed by farm vehicles without having to stop to open or close the gate. They work because cattle refuse to walk or leap over what seems to be insecure footing. The guard is made either of planks turned on edge or of two or three-inch pipe spaced no more than three inches apart. These crosspieces are mounted at ground level over a one-foot deep pit. The U. S. Department of Agriculture suggests used crankcase oil in the pit to keep down weeds and mosquitoes.

All kinds of stresses can weaken fences and shorten their life. This includes people climbing them. A stile built where fences must be crossed is an excellent idea.

Hard-line ag-college types will continue to insist that fence lines should be kept cleared of brush. I suppose those people do have an argument when they point out that such maintenance will help prevent fire damage. But when they add that the cleared fence line looks better, I find myself in disagreement. A brushy fence line looks fine to me because it has become a home for wildlife. I'll happily allow the fences to grow up in brush, to become refuges for rabbits and travel lanes for foxes. Then the fence will not only subdivide the landscape around the place but enrich it as well.

Pole Buildings

If you need an equipment or storage building, you should consider the advantages of a pole barn. When I was still a youthful farm reporter, working for a farm magazine that has since slipped quietly into oblivion, I began encountering pole barns. The idea was fresh, and it caught on rapidly. More recently, pole barns have been built with clear-span roofs, and with no supporting poles obstructing the interior of the finished building.

These barns, with the roof supported only on wall poles, give maximum use of space and make it easy to get machinery in and out. It is also simple to install large doors in them where you want. Used for livestock, they are easy to clean mechanically. And they do not place structural restrictions on sizes and shapes of pens or feed bunks. They can be equipped for cooling and heating and cause fewer injuries to livestock because there are fewer obstructions for them to crowd against.

If it is hay storage space you want, this type of structure allows easy handling of bales and is suitable for self-feeding arrangements. There is also space inside pole barns for easy handling of fruits and vegetables, even those in boxes, with fork lifts.

The wooden roof trusses can be bought already assembled, or they can be built on the farm. They should be of construction-grade Douglas fir or No. 2 kiln-dried southern yellow pine, or its equivalent. Because the joints in the trusses are the weakest part of the building, they should be glued with gusset plates made of exterior-type ½-inch or ⅝-inch plywood. The glue to use is the powdered casein type mixed with water. It should have a mold inhibitor in it.

The farm owner who needs a new pole-type building can go either of two routes: 1) he can arrange with a contractor to handle the job (in this case, he should search out a well-experienced builder), or 2) he can tackle the job on his own, after checking with someone who has built pole-type buildings and also with his county agricultural agent for plans and specifications.

CHAPTER

10

BUILDING SOIL AND

PASTURES

For more than four decades, government soil conservationists have urged better treatment for the land throughout rural America. Lectures, short courses, demonstrations, books, articles, radio and television reports by the thousands, have carried the message. But soil erosion is still a serious national problem. It contaminates watersheds, reduces fertility, and eventually lowers land values.

Early in 1977 the General Accounting Office sent to Congress a study entitled: "To Protect Tomorrow's Food Supply, Soil Conservation Needs Priority Attention." It warned that the rate of soil loss on American farms today endangers our future capacity to produce the food we need.

For its report, the GAO assembled data from a random sampling of 283 farms through the Midwest and Pacific Northwest. They found that 84 percent of these farms were losing more than five tons of soil per acre every year, causing highway maintenance problems and air and water pollution. Soil scientists believe that farm land cannot maintain its productivity if it loses more than one ton of soil per acre annually. Soil scientists also say that the creation of one inch of new soil may require at least 100 years, leaving little doubt that those who own farm land, whether it is presently in production or not, have a responsibility to keep the soil in place.

Gullies, large and small, are found in every part of the country. The nature of the soil, degree of slope, rainfall, drainage area, and vegetative cover all help determine the gravity of the gully problem.

Livestock can aggravate gullying. If you want to clear up a gullied field, it is essential to fence animals out of it. Then, with guidance from the local office of the U.S. Soil Conservation Service, you can seed the gullied area to grasses, trees, and shrubs, gradually turning it into a productive area for wildlife, or eventually for livestock.

Another step that can be taken is to divert water around the badly washed area. This strategy helps most where you want to heal small gullies that do not carry large amounts of water. Diverting water away from these gullies with a ridge or ditch slows down the runoff, keeps it away from the eroded area, and allows it to filter into the ground.

Farmers often try to stop gullying by throwing everything from old barbed wire to junked cultivators into the ditch. Dams made of brush, rocks, and logs are used to slow water. This approach can involve a lot of hand labor but may be of little help. We had one old abandoned lane, cut with gullies, that threatened to grow deeper. We first filled the gullies with brush and set small dams across them made from sections of logs held in place by stakes driven on the downhill side. This effort didn't help much. Then we disked the area, seeded it to fescue, mulched it with straw, and fertilized it to help the grass get a good start. It became one of the greenest places on the farm. The grass still holds the soil in place and the old scars are healing.

If you set out to repair a big gully, you may also have to build a diversion ditch to detour water around the area until vegetation becomes established. This objective can often be accomplished with a tractor and scraper. Bigger problem areas may require bulldozer work.

The Soil Conservation Service may also recommend various permanent structures for genuine problem areas. These structures may include concrete drop inlets to help control water from large gullies or grassed waterways. But such structures are engineering projects and usually costly ones.

Broad, shallow grass waterways that allow the runoff to flow at moderate speeds can help prevent gullies. If there is such a waterway on your land, and it is already sodded, the best plan is to leave it in sod when you plow the field. It should be at least a rod, 5½ yards wide, to spread flowing water out and cut down its force at any one point. The sides should slope gradually so that machinery can cross it easily. Soil Conservation Service technicians can help determine the proper slope and size for waterways and the best route for them to follow.

Once the waterway has been built, it should be worked into a good seedbed and treated as you would any other new grass seeding, including fertilizing in accordance with a soil test, seeding, mulching or covering the area with straw, and cultipacking, which firms the seedbed. The best times for seeding are usually early spring or late summer.

Once a waterway is established, it is important to keep it in condition with annual fertilization and with occasional mowing to maintain a dense stand of grass. It is also important to keep livestock off the waterway when the ground is wet to prevent gullies from starting.

The vegetation best for erosion control varies in different parts of the country. This too can be determined by consulting with specialists in the SCS office. One plant that has attracted attention in some northern areas is crown vetch, a European native. Highway departments in Pennsylvania favor it for its ability to form dense cover on highway embankments. Not only does it form a dense, soil-protecting mat of vegetation, spreading by underground rhizomes, but it also bears a profuse crop of purple flowers throughout much of the summer. It is drought- and cold-tolerant and will grow in thin soil.

I got a few plants of crown vetch and set them along the end of a small pond where the soil was bare. Within a year the vetch had begun to spread and cover the area. Garden stores offer the plants or seeds. Potted plants or crowns should be planted at 24-foot intervals because they will spread to fill the intervening space.

Crown vetch seed from commercial seed houses can be bought already scarified, which means the seed coating is broken or scratched to hasten germination. This is essential because of the hardness of the seed coat. The supplier should also supply the proper inoculant, or nitrogen-fixing bacteria, which crown vetch, being a legume, needs. Early spring is usually the best season for planting. One recommendation for seeding is to seed a mixture of 75 percent crown vetch and 25 percent fescue at the rate of two pounds per 1000 square feet, followed by mulching. You may need the grass to help hold the soil until the crown vetch becomes established, because this legume is sometimes slow to get started. But once started it flourishes, spreads, and binds the top soil wherever it grows. It stands up under limited grazing, but is at its best as an erosion-control plant.

Lime

From the first time I saw the place in Spoon Hollow, I realized from the flourishing crop of broomsedge that the soil was highly acidic and would require a generous application of agricultural lime for growing most crops. Acid soil is a common condition of old farms that have lost their top soil to erosion and heavy cropping, or lowlands that are poorly drained. The only way to know how much lime the land needs is to have the soil tested.

Agricultural lime should not be judged on its color or the source of the materials from which it comes. What counts, in neutralizing soil acidity is pounds of calcium and magnesium oxide per ton, plus the fineness of the grind. This information should be available from the supplier. For comparing the relative merits of different liming materials, divide the cost per ton by the total pounds of magnesium and calcium oxides per ton to get the cost per pound of oxide. The best buy is the one that gives the lowest cost per pound of these oxides.

Usually, hydrated or burnt lime will have a higher percentage of oxides but will be more costly per pound. These forms of lime may give you quicker action in correcting the acid condition of your soil. For this reason, you may want to buy enough for the garden.

Dolomitic limestones contain more than 6 percent magnesium, and this may be the best choice where a test shows the soil is low in magnesium. Limestones with less than 6 percent magnesium are known as low-magnesium or high-calcium lime.

The finer the grind, the faster the limestone will go to work correcting the acid soil condition. Fineness is measured by the percentages that will pass sieve meshes of 20, 60, and 100. It should all pass a 20-mesh screen and at least 50 percent should pass a 50-mesh screen.

Fertilizers

Several factors figure into how much fertilizer is needed on a field. Among these are the crops to be seeded, the fertility level of the soil, and the amounts of nutrients turned under as manure, or in green crops plowed down. To avoid guessing and wasting materials, have the soil tested. Use the results to guide you in applying fertilizer.

Fertilizers should be judged according to the number of pounds of plant foods they contain in relation to the cost. The three major elements in fertilizers are nitrogen (N), phosphate (P_2O_5), and potash (K_2O). Some fertilizers also have trace elements or secondary plant nutrients. These should not be used except on a prescriptive basis where soil tests show a specific need. The major fertilizer nutrients correspond to the numbers normally printed on the bag. If the bag labels the fertilizer as 5–10–15, the contents should be 5 percent available nitrogen, 10 percent phosphate, and 15 percent potash. These are what you pay for, and the remainder is inert filler material. A 50-pound bag of 10–20–20 contains the same amounts of plant food as a 100-pound bag of 5–10–10.

When fertilizing large fields, the cost of both lime and fertilizer may be lower if you have the supplier deliver and spread the materials in bulk.

Pastures

In some sections of the country, a pasture is any field too steep, rough, or rocky to grow grain crops. It becomes a pasture because this is all that is left for it. Too often it is over-grazed until the thin topsoil is gone, grass crops dwindle, and it becomes ugly and unproductive. This is the condition of pastures on many farms bought by weekend farmers. During their search for land, many buyers gravitate toward the rough hill country or other property which is less expensive.

If you need good pastures but buy rough, poverty-stricken land, you face substantial investments in getting these fields into grass and legume production. Whatever the condition of the land when you buy it, a blanket of green grass and legumes will improve the appearance, productivity, and value of the farm and will give you the satisfaction of knowing that you have treated the land well while it is in your care.

Permanent pastures are usually those that grow native grasses and legumes. These can also be improved, especially if they have been over-grazed and neglected over the years. Beginning with a soil test to determine the levels of essential elements and the acidity of the soil, such fields can be treated with lime and fertilizer to stimulate growth. Grasses need nitrogen, but if the fields have substantial growths of legumes, less nitrogen will have to be added.

Some of these old pasture fields can be brought back with fertilizing and liming alone. The improved conditions stimulate growth, and in a season or two the field may take on an entirely new character. If the fields are too heavily infested with weeds and if the grass is thin, the fields may need a complete renovation. This usually means working the field up and planting a new crop. Where fields are level enough, dry enough, and not too rocky, the renovation is begun with plowing. On fields where erosion is a threat, a field cultivator or disc is a better answer. The rough surface of the field helps catch and hold water. This preparation is generally done in the fall, and two or three tillage operations will help work the soil down and kill weeds.

Because the best techniques vary from one part of the country to another, the whole pasture-renovation procedure should be discussed with your county agricultural agent. Seeding mixtures, season of planting, fertilization, liming, and machinery to use are all points to consider. You will also need to determine whether to plant rye or some other temporary companion crop that can supply pasture, hay, or silage during that first season when the new pasture seeding is becoming established.

If soil tests show that the field needs liming, the lime should be worked into the soil two or three months before the new crop is seeded, giving it time to change the level of acidity in the soil.

If you want pastures capable of really heavy forage production, the best answer may not be permanent pastures. The best answer may be semi-permanent grass seedings, to be reseeded when the stand begins to show signs of aging and thinning. These are usually the taller, heavier-producing forage species, for example, a mixture of alfalfa and brome grass on well-drained soils, or birdsfoot trefoil and timothy where soils are less well drained.

Failure of seedings is costly in dollars and loss of grazing time. The agronomists suggest definite steps for insurance against seeding failures. First, lime and fertilizer needs are important. Second, so is killing the old sod. Otherwise competition from less productive plants will cut into forage production. Third, you should prepare a proper seedbed, whether by plowing, disking, or cultivating.

Plant the seed shallow. One of the best tools for this operation is a grain drill adapted for band seeding. After the seeding, treat the field with the cultipacker. This machine helps firm the seed in the seedbed so it will be in contact with moisture.

Time of seeding is important, and the county agent will know the best local answer. Buy quality seed, and be sure that legume seed is properly inoculated with the suitable strain of bacteria before planting, enabling it to fix nitrogen and enrich the soil.

Finally, do not graze the new seeding heavily, if at all, the first year. It should not be grazed less than five or six inches, and should be given at least a month of freedom to grow ungrazed in the fall before cold weather halts growth. After these steps, and adapting them to local recommendations, you should produce high-yielding pastures.

Queen of Forage Crops

There is nothing more beautiful to the farmer than a field green with thick-growing alfalfa—the "queen of the forages." And the beauty is dollar deep. Alfalfa is a heavy producer of high-value feed at relatively low cost. Five to eight tons of quality hay per acre is common, and alfalfa grows even in years too dry for good row crop yields. This is feed packed with vitamins and minerals as well as protein. Cut early, it contains 20 to 25 percent crude protein. Agronomists have trouble finding enough nice things to say about this crop, and so do farmers who grow it.

In addition to its qualities as a feed, it is a nitrogen-fixing legume: it improves the fertility levels of soils and helps give a higher protein content to companion grasses grown with it, with lower investments in nitrogen fertilizer.

Alfalfa, however, is not a crop that will prosper on infertile soil. So when you select a field for it, choose the better soil. The alfalfa field can be on rolling land, but the soil must be productive and the land must have good drainage.

In addition, the soil must not be highly acidic. Alfalfa needs a pH level of 6.5 to 7.0. A soil test is important in determining how much lime to add to the field and also the amounts of potash and phosphate needed.

A good seedbed is essential for germination and early growth. Once the field is plowed, it should be disked and harrowed until the soil clumps are worked down to an inch or smaller in diameter. Otherwise, seeds will fall into deep spaces and not come up. Alfalfa seed should never be planted more than ¾ inch deep.

To find the best seeding time for your area, check with your county agent. Stick to varieties the agent recommends for your area, and buy the best quality seed you can find.

Once you establish a good field of alfalfa, you must still maintain it properly. This may mean adding fertilizer or lime as needed, depending on the results of soil tests. Alfalfa grows rapidly. Harvested for hay, it yields a first cutting early in the season, plus additional cuttings. Take the first cutting as soon as you find the alfalfa budding and before it blooms. Tests have shown that the total digestible nutrients (TDN) in the first cutting of alfalfa will drop as much as 20 percent if the first cutting is delayed too long. It is better to take this cutting early and settle for the higher nutrient level than let it grow to gain more bulk in the harvest.

The alfalfa stand will hold up and produce longer if you let one of the later cuttings go until the alfalfa is in half or three-quarter bloom.

CHAPTER

11

DO YOU NEED A TRACTOR?

The arrival of the modern tractor on the farm scene was a major labor-saving factor in the agricultural revolution that sent farm lads to the cities seeking work. But for the person owning a small farm today, buying a tractor may not be practical. Many owners of small farms want a tractor because they like to drive one, and because they can think of tasks the machine will simplify.

One of my semi-retired friends owns a 23-acre farm where he goes in the middle of the week and stays through the weekend, working his garden, riding his horses, and improving the little white frame house. His farm had kept him busy and happy, but he wanted a tractor. True, he could have survived without it by having a neighbor plow his garden and come in with the bush hog to knock down the weeds.

The question was finally settled when he bought a neighbor's used tractor for $750. Acquiring that tractor did as much for the owner's morale as buying the farm had done in the first place. He put it to work hauling fire wood, plowing the garden, and mowing the weeds. But part of its value was psychological.

"A farm's not a farm without a tractor," he told me.

I too continue to think about buying a tractor, but I keep putting it off. Even old used ones are high-priced now, and there's only limited work for one around our place. Including the weed cutting and wood hauling, I would probably find only a few full days of work a year for it. If I bought a tractor, it would be useless without a bush hog for weed cutting, a cart for hauling, a set of plows, and probably a blade for scraping the lane.

A better answer for us was a deal worked out with our neighbor at the head of the hollow. I agreed to rent his tractor a day at a time when I had work for it and he didn't need it. A tractor, and its accompanying equipment, uses energy and natural resources. It makes sense to me for neighboring farmers to pool machinery whenever possible to get maximum use from it.

Unfortunately, you can't always arrange to use another farmer's equipment. Work schedules often conflict. If both farmers are operating commercial farms, each will have seasonal jobs with critical timing, and each must have his own equipment.

When you do set out to buy a tractor today, you're immediately confronted with a wide choice. Within the tractor family are models ranging from the little garden or estate tractors to giant machines made for pulling rows of plows. The choice should fit both your need and your financial limitations.

Here again, it's good business in your preliminary planning to get as much advice and professional help as you can. Other farmers, the county agent, and your farm equipment salesman can all contribute, and one of them may even lead you to a good buy in just the machine you need. You may want to buy a new tractor, but there are also several ways—including the authorized tractor outlets—to find good used farm machinery. Other possibilities are the classified sections of the county newspaper, and the farm auctions that are advertised. If you're going to an auction to bid on a tractor, find out in advance what the model offered should bring. You should have the opportunity, prior to bidding, to inspect the machine and hear it run. You will want to consider the general appearance of the tractor and whether or not it has been well cared for, the condition of the rubber, and the number of hours on it or its age. How recently it has had the engine serviced can be important. Before bidding gets underway have a top limit in mind and stick to it.

Care of the tractor is important. It should have a regular schedule for maintenance, and it should be stored indoors. If your

For big jobs such as plowing, your best approach may be to hire a neighbor rather than own a tractor yourself.

Today's small tractors can do many fairly big jobs such as the plowing this one is doing here.

farm is left unattended much of the time, you will want a building where machinery can be locked up. The tractor, and its attachments, are costly equipment. But if they're well maintained, protected, and properly handled, they can last many years.

A person new to farming, or without tractor-operating experience, should be briefed on handling a tractor before climbing aboard to set the machine in motion. Every year there are fatal accidents when tractors roll over on their operators, or when loose clothing gets tangled in power-take-off attachments.

CHAPTER

12

THE ROTARY TILLER
SAVES LABOR

I had never owned a rotary tiller, or even operated one. They came on the country scene after I had moved to the city. But once we acquired our farm, and I marked off a substantial garden space, the necessity of a rotary tiller became obvious. I had witnessed the work of these powerful little machines as they snorted across gardens leaving the earth worked up in a fine seedbed.

Somewhere I read in a garden magazine that the best way to start off is to rent a rotary tiller and try it out, which may be the best course for some people. But I am not certain what this is supposed to tell you. A single use is not enough to teach you how to use the machine—those early hours of operation would certainly be the roughest for the operator. Renting might tell me that I didn't want a rotary tiller after all, which was not what I wanted to learn. If others could handle a tiller, and obviously thousands could, then so could I. Besides, the minimum daily rate at our neighborhood rental agency was $20. If, after shopping around, I could buy a new one for $200, that one day's rental would simply add 10 percent to my rotary tiller cost, and I still wouldn't be getting accustomed to the same machine I'd end up owning and using.

I talked with a couple of neighbors who had experience with

rotary tillers and whose fine gardens gave testimony to their knowledge. Then, armed with their advice, buying seemed even more logical than renting, so I started shopping.

When I arrived at the farm the next time, I had a large cardboard box in which were packed all the parts. I attached the handle complete with throttle and clutch, then slipped the rotary knives onto the axle and secured them with the pins provided. One other element of the machine that must be attached and set is the brake stake, a steel bar that runs in the ground and determines the depth at which the rotary tiller will dig. A series of holes on the stake permit you to set it deep or shallow by where you set the pin that holds it in position. Finally I filled the machine with the recommended grade of oil, and the tank with gas.

With everything ready for the initial test run, I set the throttle, pulled out the choke, and gave the starter cord a couple of pulls.

The rotary tiller can do a great deal of heavy work for the gardener.

The engine snorted to life. I let it warm up briefly before setting the machine on its first row.

The brake stake can be set for a shallow first run over the area, then adjusted for another trip over for deeper tillage. But once you are sure of your machine you can set it for deeper tillage. It handles more easily working deep than shallow and moves more slowly. The speed, however, can be set with the throttle. Until you've conquered the techniques of running the tiller, a moderate speed will make it easier to handle.

Any machine can give a new driver some surprises on that first trip. My initial trip across the garden was rough. This machine is not a substitute for a plow or even a disk harrow. Under average soil conditions, the rotary tiller should be used after both plow and disk. In light, friable soil, with the right moisture content and no vegetation to turn under, it might prepare a seedbed without prior plowing. The tiller bucked and pulled from side to side. By the time I reached the end of that row I was ready to stop and think through what I was doing. I heaved the tiller around by brute strength, disengaged the clutch handle, cut the throttle to an idling speed, and stood there.

I thought back to the day my father first let me cultivate the corn crop with a one-horse cultivator. The situation was comparable. I must have been about ten at the time, and highly apprehensive. A little dip to the right or left, and suddenly out would come one of those hills of corn or maybe several hills, unless I could correct the cultivator's course quickly. The horse plodded steadily along between the two rows while I, with a tense grip on the cultivator handles, stumbled along behind him concentrating on the direction of the plow blades. By the end of that first quarter-mile row, I was worn out and breathing heavily. My arms hung like rubber bands. I had seen others, including my father, cultivate all day long behind a horse, and I couldn't believe they were so much stronger.

That was the day I learned not to manhandle a cultivator and try to pit my strength against that of the horse. Instead of heaving the cultivator to one side as it went off course, all I had to do was put a gentle guiding pressure on the handle. This turned it back and corrected its course. After that, the job of plowing corn behind the old horse became almost pleasurable. The same principle applies to the rotary tiller. If you try to handle it by brute force, it is not a labor-saving device. Instead, learn to correct it with minimum effort. After a round or two, the rotary tiller and I were making progress.

These machines are not easily turned at the end of the row. They crawl forward on their tiller blades, not the two little rubber-tired wheels. The wheels are up out of the way when the machine is at work. When you're turning the tiller 180 degrees at the end of the garden, you soon learn to slow down, or to make wide turns. There is no reason for making the return trip right alongside the path cut on the previous trip. One common practice is to swing the tiller around in a wide turn, leaving one width of the blades between the new strip and the old and catching this in-between strip on the way back. Then if the soil is not worked up well enough, you may want to work the garden over at right angles to the original strips.

The rotary tiller is not easily wheeled around when the engine is not operating. It can be pushed on the wheels with the brake stake up by pushing down on the handles and lifting the blades off the ground. Or it can be pulled backwards, because the brake stake is only locked in place for forward movement.

Many rotary tillers made today are equipped with a reverse so they can be backed under power. But this should be done slowly and carefully on areas where the machine will not get away from you. The clutch, which is controlled by a grip on the handle, is automatically disengaged the instant you release your grip on it. It can, however, be locked in place for easier operation on those long clean sweeps across the garden.

Soil condition is important to a good tilling job. If the soil is too wet, it sticks together and dries into clods that may last throughout the entire season, making garden work much more difficult. Take a handful of freshly plowed soil and squeeze it. The soil should fall apart when your hand is opened and not cling together in a mud ball.

Sometimes the rotary blades will accumulate mud and become entangled in weeds and grass. In this case, stop the machine, turn off the engine, and clean the blades. There is no other safe way.

These machines will do more jobs than simply preparing a

seedbed. Depending on which brand you choose, you can buy additional styles of blades for different tasks. Even if you have only the one set of blades, by different arrangements, you can use them for a variety of chores. Instead of using all four blades, you can remove the two end blades and use the machine for weeding and cultivating between narrow rows.

But check your dealer to see if the manufacturer offers other attachments. For some rotary tillers you can buy a special weeding attachment. Or you can buy a single heavy blade for furrowing. If you want to make ridges for certain plants, such as sweet potatoes, or for irrigated fields, you can buy shovels that build ridges. In addition, you can get shovels designed for making rows for planting, or even a small bulldozer blade for scraping and shaping sand and gravel on the farm lane, or for snow removal.

One thing I like about the rotary tiller is that it requires far less care than the old horse it replaced. But the machine's care is vital to long life. Follow the manufacturer's instructions, especially on the grade of oil in the engine and the frequency of changing it. Before starting the engine, check the oil level every time. These engines operate at high speeds and work heavily. Low oil levels can cause fast wear.

The air filter should be cleaned often because it keeps dust out of engine cylinder and the carburetor. A clean air filter means more efficient burning of fuel.

Go over the machine occasionally to see that all nuts and bolts and screws are tight. With the engine turned off, take all the tangled weeds and grass out of the tines so the engine does not have to labor harder to fight the drag of these materials when it is put to work. Foreign materials lodged in the machine's working parts also provide places for moisture to collect and rust to start. The rotary tiller can be cleaned with the garden hose. Wash off the dust and mud, and then let the tiller dry in the sun.

CHAPTER
13

THE LITTLE TOOLS

At first, you may not have a tractor, bush hog, or chain saw. But from the beginning, you are going to find a multitude of uses for various common hand tools on your country place. Even if you have never been handy with tools, this is the time to become better acquainted. Our neighbor on the township road at the head of the hollow worked in an office before he and his wife moved to the country a few years ago. He claims that prior to the move he never built anything more complicated than a door stop. But he soon found that he could conquer jobs he'd never considered before. He found that he took pride in building his own fences, adding a room, and putting a new roof on his house.

A set of tools grows as your needs change. I began by putting hammer, saw, screw driver, a pair of pliers, and some assorted nails and screws into an open box carried in the back of the vehicle when we drove out to the farm. I still carry a tool box, but now it's a metal tool chest. To the original collection I've added new pieces of equipment handy for various jobs around the farm.

Here's a list of the hand tools I consider important for general use around the farm:

Claw hammer	Hand saw
Square	Hack saw

Assorted screw drivers	Pliers
Set of auger bits	Oil stone
Ratchet brace	Monkey wrench
Measuring tape or ruler	Crow bar

A vise becomes highly useful also. You'll need a workbench for mounting it. When you've gone this far, you might as well designate a special location for your shop and tools if space is available under roof. A row of nails in the wall will keep many of the tools in place. If this is not neat enough, you can put a sheet of peg board on the wall over the work bench and buy special hooks for it to hold the tools. This arrangement helps avoid nicked edges on cutting tools. We were fortunate in finding that the previous owners had built a heavy work bench in the tractor shed and even left an ancient vise mounted there. I believe in getting the full use out of such instruments and feel no temptation to replace the vise with a new one. The manufacture of tools uses natural resources from iron ore to energy, so I keep the old ones in service as long as they do the job well and are safe to use.

You'll find as you go about your country place that you probably carry one or two tools with you most of the time. A pair of pliers can help with many an unanticipated task. A northwoods guide with whom I once traveled had a good idea. He had fashioned a belt holster for his pliers and always had them at his fingertips. A pocketknife has even more jobs than a pair of pliers. My first preference is a small knife that handles a wide variety of jobs but is not hard to carry.

Aside from implements in the tool box, you'll need some basic garden and lawn tools. You can buy these new or you may pick them up at local auctions. Those bought at a neighborhood farm auction should serve well if the metal parts are not broken or badly rusted and if the handles are solid and tight. But if they are flimsy or poorly made, you're better off going to the hardware store to pick out good ones. The basic implements I acquired include a hoe, rake, mattock, longhandled shovel, spade, and sledge hammer.

Time spent caring for hand tools is time well spent. The key words are clean and sharp. The best time to clean tools is right after a job is finished. Hoes and shovels should not go back into

*Community farm sales sometimes offer an excellent
opportunity for you to buy needed hand tools and
machinery at bargain prices.*

the shed with dirt on them because it dries there and is then
really difficult to remove. Meanwhile, the metal is rusting. Often
you can clean a tool sufficiently by wiping it on the grass or cleaning off the mud with a stick. But a better way is to stick the working end into a bucket of water or hold it under the garden hose.
Then wipe it dry with a cloth. As a final step, go over it once
lightly with an oily rag to keep it from rusting.

Tight handles are important, especially in such tools as axes
and hammers, because they mean greater safety and are easier
to work with. Occasionally, you may have to put a new screw in
the handle of a hoe or wedges in the head of the axe or sledge
hammer to tighten them.

For sharpening most tools, you should keep a sharpening stone
and file. Tools being sharpened are usually held in the vise. It is
worth remembering that the "tang" of the file, the small pointed
end, can jab into your palm. Some people fit a round wooden
handle over the tang to prevent this. Many a corn cob has also
served for this purpose.

When driving around the farm, you may have a problem with
long-handled tools. Often there is no easy way to carry them.
Some people have a long wooden box in their truck bed to provide
a place for tools. I have an old carpet that goes on the bed of the
pickup to keep tools from bouncing around. I can usually lay
them on the carpet and brace them with other equipment to
keep them from rattling around when I drive.

Two systems of helping to keep things shipshape around the farm tool area are a rack that holds containers made of empty cans with tops removed, and a suspended jar holder that lets you see contents and rotates for easy access.

CHAPTER
14
CHAIN SAWS

Among the first tools that the new farm owner may need is a chain saw. This mechanical marvel has relegated the old cross cut saw to antique status. The chain saw is a fast answer to land-clearing jobs where fields of brush and woody vegetation, too big for a bush hog, must be removed. The chain saw finds additional work in cutting fence posts and in felling or pruning trees. It can even be used for rough sawing of lumber. Or you can easily cut cross sections of logs to be used for patio blocks.

The biggest job for my chain saw is harvesting firewood to keep the house warm in winter. With an hour's work I can cut a week-end supply, and in a couple of days I can stack up enough fire-wood to last the winter.

The chain saw has some faults. Whoever uses it must accept its high noise level, the element of danger, and often its cantan-kerous mechanical nature.

Chain saws are driven by two-cycle engines fueled with a mix-ture of gasoline and oil. The working element is a continuous chain of notched saw teeth running around a guide bar. When you set out to buy a new chain saw, it's a good idea to investigate several brands. A small or lightweight chain saw may perform all the work you have for it. If you choose one too heavy, it can be tiring to operate. My choice was a medium-sized saw with a 14-inch bar, capable of cutting across a log with a 28-inch diameter. The ideal way would be to cut with a saw before you purchase. But if you're new to chain saws, you won't learn enough about them in half an hour to help you make a choice. Important qualities are light weight, good balance, and minimum vibration.

The speeding chain on your saw requires a constant supply of lubricant. The saw has a reservoir for chain oil, which is applied to the chain in one of two ways. Until recently chain saws were oiled manually with a button you could push at intervals while the saw was in operation. Major manufacturers have developed automatic oiling systems, a big improvement. But even saws with automatic oiling may need additional oil during an especially tough cutting job. For this reason, in addition to the automatic oiling equipment, the saw usually is equipped with a manual oiling button. Every time I refuel my saw I also refill the chain-oil reservoir. If it doesn't need chain oil then, the chances are good that the automatic oiling mechanism isn't working.

Some manufacturers market their own brand of chain oil; they may also offer their own mixture of fuel oil. Generally it is cheaper to mix the fuel oil yourself, paying careful attention to the recommended proportions of gasoline and oil printed either in the instruction book or on the saw itself. It's a good idea to have a cloth or brush handy when refilling your saw so you can clean off the area around the caps to prevent sawdust from getting into the fuel or oil tanks.

Some chain saws are difficult to start. The usual procedure is to turn the switch button on, open the choke, and pull the starter cord sharply. While this is done, the saw should be held firmly in position on a log or on the ground. With some types you can place the saw on the ground and use one foot in the back handle of the saw, one hand on the front handle and the other hand to pull the starter cord. Starting instructions are usually included in the operator's manual. One saw that I used had a starter cord prone to come off its drum when pulled to full length. This flaw caused a big delay and considerable difficulty in getting the cord rewrapped properly on the drum. I noticed that one of my neighbors, experienced with chain saws, never pulled the cord the full distance.

Starting the saw may require several pulls of the cord. As soon as the engine seems about ready to start, turn the choke off. In the next pull or two of the cord, the engine should sputter to life. Let the engine warm up for a couple of minutes before starting to cut.

There's an element of common sense in the safe operation of a chain saw, and the person using one should keep his mind on the job. Until you get the feel of the machine, settle for a simple cutting job, such as bucking logs into stove lengths. Keep your feet and body in a position that is comfortable and secure, put the chain saw into gear, and watch it eat its way through the wood.

The chain should fit the chain bar. This element should be checked before the engine is started, each time the saw is used. If the chain can be turned by hand around the chain bar, and lifted enough to see the bottoms of two teeth, the tension should be about right. Saws normally come with tools to help set the chain bars for proper tension. The instruction book tells how. If the chain needs to be tightened, it is better to make the adjustment when the saw is cold.

Carburetor trouble is not uncommon. If the saw idles too fast, the chain may revolve even though it is not in gear. This is a highly dangerous condition. You can adjust the carburetor yourself or return it to the shop for service, depending on your own skill and level of confidence. Whatever the answer, the saw that is going to cut properly and operate safely must be in top condition.

Keep the teeth on the chain sharp. There are two ways to do this. The saw can be taken to the shop and sharpened by a professional at a cost of $3 to $6, or the teeth can be sharpened at home. Most chain-saw manufacturers sell a chain-sharpening kit, including a round file and a metal guide to help you file the teeth at the proper angle. One kit costs the price of three or four commercial sharpenings. But after you've sharpened a saw a couple of times and caught on to the idea, it's not a big mysterious job. It can be done in ten minutes or so. When the chain is dull, it doesn't cut fast. The dull chain throws sawdust; the sharp one, woodchips.

If you cut through a log and allow the chain to touch the ground, almost certainly it is going to require sharpening. Rocks seem to have a way of being there. But dirt will also dull the chain, and a hidden nail or piece of barbed wire will do it no good at all. If you're cutting a log on the ground, don't cut all the way through it. Instead, cut most of the way, roll the log over, and make a new cut to meet the first one.

When it becomes necessary to cut a living tree, there is a certain satisfaction in dropping it where you want it to fall. Always approach the job with extreme care. Wind direction and tree size should be taken into consideration along with whether or not the tree is leaning. First start by cutting a deep notch in the tree on the side toward which you want it to fall. The V-shaped notch should be perpendicular to the axis of the tree trunk on the bottom, with the top of the cut sloping in to meet it at the back of the notch. Next, make a cut from the opposite side, aiming at the bottom of the notch. This is a job that should be tried on smaller trees until experience prepares you for tackling the big jobs. Even a small tree can be a hazard if it falls in the wrong direction. The wood cutter who finds that he has miscalculated and that the tree is leaning toward him and binding the saw should abandon the machine and escape.

Loose clothing, long coats, or flying scarves are hazards. The careful chain-saw operator wears a safety hat and safety goggles.

Also take steps to prevent loss of hearing. These powerful two-cycle engines are among man's noisier inventions. There is no doubt that they can damage hearing. The risk is in proportion to both the noise level of the saw and the length of time it is used. This loss of hearing can be permanent. Wear ear plugs or a pair of muffs. These can be bought in industrial supply houses or gun shops.

Kickback can occur when the upper portion of the front of the chain bar touches a solid object while the saw is in motion. This object might be another limb during a pruning operation or a rock when cutting a log lying on the ground. The energy from the engine may force the saw out of the cut and upward making it kick back toward the operator. Manufacturers have perfected kickback safety devices that help avoid this hazard, and you'll want to consider them in your choice of a chain saw.

Here are some safety rules which should always be followed:

A chain saw can make quick work of a project such as turning poles into a corral. Note that the operator is wearing safety glasses.

1. Carry the saw by the handle only.
2. Before starting to cut, inspect trees carefully for loose limbs and rot. (You cannot hear a rotten limb break when the saw is going.)
3. Clean out around the tree or the log so the chain does not catch on anything.
4. When felling a tree, choose your escape path in advance. Be sure that there are no briar patches or other obstructions to slow you down.
5. Wear heavy shoes or boots with non-skid soles.
6. Leave the chain saw solidly positioned on the ground or on the log while starting the engine.
7. Keep a firm grip on the handles when sawing, and keep the saw in a position where you can control it.
8. Shut off the engine anytime the saw is not actually in use. This precaution prevents damage to both the chain and the operator.

CHAPTER
15

THE FARMER'S PICKUP

Before we bought our farm, I had never owned a pickup truck. I suddenly found that I needed something to haul fence posts, fertilizer, baled straw, and tools. I chose a club cab, which gives the dog a place to ride behind the seat and also makes room for camera cases and luggage if we should decide to drive the truck on trips. The club cab has two jump seats that are satisfactory for people of modest size on short rides.

The truck, when I finally drove it off the lot, had many of the features considered desirable on modern passenger cars. It had power steering and power brakes. I also wanted cruise control so I could set a selected speed on the highway and then ride along with my foot off the accelerator. I also ordered the heavy-duty undercoat because I expect the truck to last for several years.

Finally, we drove to the local camping-vehicle store and picked out a top to cover the truck bed. If need be, it can be taken off by removing half a dozen bolts. Some tops are secured with clamps, but the bolts seemed a better choice because of the rough roads we were certain to drive.

One of the first things we learned from this pickup truck was that it provides an easy ride. On long drives we found that we did not tire as quickly, sitting up on the bench-like seats, as when cradled in the bucket seats of the modern passenger car. On the strength of this experience, we decided that we would drive it on the next long trip we had to make.

The opportunity came within a few months when I had to go to the West Coast on business. Several full days of driving sold us on the comfort of the truck, and we liked the improved visibility offered from the high seats that put you in a better position to observe traffic. The cab, however, is a little noisier than a passenger car. The gasoline milage is comparable to that averaged on most large American-made passenger cars. But the pickup is a farm vehicle ready for a wide variety of hauling jobs.

Today most pickup trucks are sold not to farmers but to people seeking a good combination work-recreation vehicle. However, the pickup truck remains the standard rural vehicle. You need only go to a farm auction, or into the county seat on a Saturday afternoon, to learn this.

If you're looking for a combination work vehicle and passenger car, the pickup truck is your likely choice. This one has optional cover over back.

You may be tempted to consider four-wheel drive. Owning a four-wheel drive vehicle will give you a feeling of go-anywhere invulnerability, but ask yourself if you really need it. It may be essential if you drive across your fields and over rough terrain. But driving gravel roads to reach the farm is not really an argument for four-wheel drive. Thousands of vehicles with two-wheel power drive gravel roads everyday, some of them rough indeed. Instead of four-wheel drive you may settle for a set of tires with special tread to give you better traction in the rough going, and the mud and snow. Mud and snow tires are not especially noisy or rougher riding than standard tires.

Vehicles with four-wheel drive are likely to be less comfortable than those with two-wheel drive. The four-wheel drive sets the truck higher in the air. The cab may be harder to get into and out of. Such vehicles may still have plush bucket seats, carpeting, and other luxurious comforts. These features, however, are designed for the fun seekers more than for the farm trade.

The older four-wheel drive system enabled the driver to disengage the front wheel drive when it was not needed, either with levers from the cab, or by turning the front hubs. Today there are some pickup trucks that keep the front-wheel drive engaged full time.

If you will do much driving over rocky terrain where sharp edges may damage the underside of the vehicle, you may want to order a set of skid plates. These can be bolted to the bottom of the vehicle to protect the working parts and still be removed for major repairs.

Farm owners sometimes find that a winch on the front of the truck is a blessing. If the truck gets stuck in a ditch, you can hook the winch cable to a tree and "walk" the car out onto solid footing. And you can use the winch to move rocks, logs, and machinery.

You may consider an auxiliary fuel tank, especially if your farm is back in the boondocks, or if you travel at night when rural service stations are normally closed. The preferable arrangement for convenience is to have the pipes for filling both tanks on the same side of the truck.

Experience with my pickup has taught me its shortcomings as well as its advantages. The longer wheel base needed for a club cab model requires more space for turning.

There will probably be a label on the door of your truck that tells you the gross vehicle weight. This is the maximum weight for the vehicle and load, including people. Remember that the weight of optionals will cut down the pay-load your truck can handle. The curb weight listed for the truck includes standard equipment and full tank of fuel. The gross axle weight, listed on the label attached to the door frame, tells you the maximum weight allowed for each axle.

16

THE GARDEN PLOT

One thing we did shortly after taking possession of our property was begin choosing a place for the garden. The family garden has made a comeback. High food prices, the need for regular exercise, concern about chemicals in food, and the belief that a home garden is the way to have high-quality vegetables all played a role in our plan to have a garden. There is also great satisfaction in growing your own foods.

One problem was soon apparent. There had been no garden on the old farm for several years, and I couldn't even tell where it might have been. A small level plot across the lane where the old barn stood was rejected because of excess moisture.

First, I wanted a soil that was fertile, well-drained, and loose (friable) so it worked up easily. There was no such location. Wherever we'd make the garden, the soil would have to be improved.

Sunlight is important, so I ruled out areas close to buildings or shade trees. Trees and shrubs can also compete with the vegetables for food and moisture. As protection against the threat of late and early frost, I passed up low areas that might hold pockets of cold air.

In addition, I wanted a location close enough to the house for the garden to be worked whenever we happened to have short periods of spare time, and where it could be better guarded against animals.

The final choice was a narrow space beside the lane that follows the ridge to the back of the farm. There was space for a garden plot 30 feet wide by 100 feet long, ample for our needs. It was covered by a heavy grass sod. From the beginning, I faced the fact that this would not be a good garden area for three or four years until we could build up its fertility and soil tilth.

After the first plowing, our plot looked impossible. Strips of the dark green grass showed between the half-turned furrows. Disking worked it down somewhat but still left it rough. In addition, the clay nature of the soil helped hold it in clods no matter how much we worked it. The rotary tiller moved it around but didn't seem to break it up the way I had hoped.

The first year we produced a fair crop of garden beans, which are easily produced. Most other crops did poorly to moderately well. But we were looking ahead to the second year and took positive steps to improve the garden's potential.

A good garden soil is high in organic matter, deep and friable, a living environment for a host of soil organisms. If the soil is too heavy, it stays too wet and is difficult to till. But soil too sandy seldom holds water well enough and often lacks fertility. The good garden soil lies somewhere between heavy clay and the light sandy soils.

Our neighbor, Chuck Dillon, and I talked about the problem when he came to plow it that fall in anticipation of the second year's garden. He brought his big diesel tractor this time.

"We'll plow it deep," he said.

Those plows must have cut down to 12 inches. All the old growth from the first year's garden was neatly turned under. Still the soil held together tightly, revealing its clay nature.

A few weeks later Chuck drove down the lane again. This time he had his truck.

"I brought you what that garden needs," he announced.

He had bought a ton of bagged ground limestone, half for his garden and half for mine. We threw the bags off along the garden, I paid my share of the cost and waved to Chuck as he drove off up the lane out of the hollow.

The structure of this heavy clay soil will be improved by the application of lime. Have your soil tested to see whether it requires lime or some other treatment.

Your county agent will assure you that too much lime can be just as bad as too little, and I would not argue the point. The answer, he will add, is to be found in soil tests, and again I agree. But there was evidence that the garden plot needed some of this lime. The broomsedge growing on the hillside, the thin soil, and the absence of clover of any kind were all indicators. So, feeling slightly guilty about not waiting for the results of a soil test, I cut open the bags and spread the limestone with a shovel evenly over the garden. Depending on the acidity of the soil and the level to which you want the pH raised, the soil test may call for two, three, or four tons of lime per acre. For translating these rates to smaller plots, remember that two tons per acre is about the same as nine pounds per 100 square feet, three tons per acre is 14 pounds for 100 square feet, and four tons per acre is 18 pounds for 100 square feet. Having confessed this, I still suggest proceeding on the basis of soil tests so you know the needs and can supply them acordingly.

Soil Tests

State agricultural colleges generally maintain soil-testing facilities where samples of soil, sent in by farmers and gardeners, are tested. Recommendations are then made for various crops. Usually the county agricultural agent has information on the procedure, the best time of year for testing, and the cost. The big challenge is to take a soil sample that is representative of the field sampled. According to one state college of agriculture, as many as one sample out of five taken gives poor information, leading to inaccurate recommendations. Reasons cited include: 1) taking samples from too few locations, 2) contamination from containers containing traces of lime, fertilizer, detergents, or other materials, 3) sampling to the wrong soil depth, and 4) taking frozen samples or from soil too wet.

The following steps are recommended by soil specialists for taking soil samples:

Combine enough samplings to get a composite that will reflect the nature of the field. This may be 30 or more borings in fields of 10 acres or more, or where the field has been heavily fertilized in recent years. Even a garden plot should be tested through a composite of several borings. Depth of the sample is important. First remove organic debris from the soil. For vegetable gardens, sample the soil to plow depth. Meadows should be sampled at four to six inches, established lawns at two inches. The best tool for taking a sample is an auger or hollow tube to take a core. A garden spade or trowel, carefully used, will accomplish the same thing. Mix the samples from a field in a clean bucket, and transfer a sample to a clean bag, which is usually supplied by the agricultural extension service. Wet soil should be air-dried (not oven-dried) prior to mailing. Soil samples taken in the fall are best. They should not be taken for several months after the field has been treated with lime or fertilizer. A garden should be soil-tested every two to three years, lawns every three to five years, fields in rotation once per rotation, and fields planted to continuous row crops once every year or two.

That lime application of ours made a remarkable change in the nature of our garden soil. By the following spring, it had turned into a friable, easily-worked garden. Chuck had said he would come down in spring and disk the garden when he did his own. But that was the winter he took a trip to Texas, bought a shrimp boat, and called home to tell his son to sell his big tractor. My garden went without disking. But the rototiller worked it up beautifully, something it could not do a year earlier.

There remained the matter of organic materials. What I would have preferred at this stage was enough half-rotted cow and horse manure to cover the garden with a two inch-thick blanket before plowing.

But there were still some steps that could be taken to enrich the organic content of the top soil. One way is to plant rye as a green manure crop. This should be done in late summer and plowed under with a nitrogen application. In addition, clippings, leaves, old hay, and other organic materials can be collected and composted. (See compost page 115.) The high organic content of the top soil helps the garden hold moisture, creates good living conditions for desirable soil organisms, and provides fertility and the conditions under which plant nutrients are best utilized by the growing crops. Vigorous-growing garden crops, produced on rich soil with high organic content, also suffer less damage from disease and insects than do plants growing under stress on thin soils.

Two factors should play a large role in determining what you grow in your garden: the foods your family enjoys, and the crops you are best able to produce. Some garden crops take more space

Organic materials, which are important in improving the tilth and fertility of garden soil, can come from many sources including—as here—aquatic plants gathered from the farm pond.

than many gardeners can allot to them. Included are cucumbers, squash, cantaloupe, and watermelons. The larger the garden, the more space you may devote to such crops. But in the small garden, the better choices are usually the highly productive vegetables such as beans, tomatoes, peppers, cabbage, beets, and onions.

There is no way to lay out a single garden plan that will serve all purposes and all gardeners equally well. Part of the pleasure of gardening comes in planning and fitting the garden to the family needs. But the planning can play a role in how much work the garden will require. Typically, farm people once had two gardens, a small kitchen garden for lettuce, radishes, onions, and the like, and a larger plot for corn, potatoes, pumpkins, and cucumbers. This arrangement may still be worth considering.

Gardening is largely a spring activity. Spring is the season of new promise, and everyone who gardens has the itch to get started. The aim is to get the early crops into the ground as soon as the danger of a late frost passes.

Planning the garden can be done during the winter on a sheet of paper that becomes a map of what you hope the garden will be. This early planning gives you time to work out the best system for maximum yields. Start with an outline of the garden drawn to scale, and on this, locate the rows and the direction they will run. On slopes, rows should follow the contour. Add dates for planting, spacing of plants in the row, and whether another crop is to follow in the same space. Where possible, plan for long rows because these save time in garden chores. There is no rule against planting more than one crop in the same row, provided the distance needed between rows is similar for the crops planted. Plan the rows of taller crops, such as sweet corn, so they will not shade the shorter plants.

The old trick of stretching a string between stakes is as effective today as it ever was in helping a gardener plant straight rows of beans.

The time of planting can be critical. Some crops are strictly warm-weather plants; others prosper better in cool weather. Even ahead of the frost-free date, you can get some garden crops into the ground if the soil can be worked up into a seedbed. Four to six weeks ahead of the frost-free date, according to the U.S. Department of Agriculture, the following crops can be safely planted in most years: broccoli, cabbage, lettuce, onions, peas, potatoes, spinach, and turnips. From two to four weeks before the frost-free date, you can plant radishes, parsnips, beets, carrots, and chard. Wait for the frost-free date, however, before planting beans, okra, squash, sweet corn, and tomatoes.

You may have a temptation to play your hunches and try to beat the season a few days with the tomato plants, but it's safer to wait until the danger of frost is gone and avoid the need to re-plant. Wait until a week or more after the frost-free date before planting eggplant, peppers, sweet potatoes, melons, and cucumbers. For late planting, usually six to eight weeks ahead of the first autumn frost, you can put in beets, collard, kale, lettuce, turnips, and spinach, all hardy cool-weather plants.

In some warmer parts of the country, the garden can produce a succession of crops nearly the year around. Even in northern states, your garden can often produce more than a single crop. Here are some typical crop successions: early potatoes followed by turnips or spinach; and an early crop of peas or beans followed by planting late cabbage, celery, carrots, and beets. Some gardeners even get the second crop started between the rows before the first crop is harvested. It is best not to follow a crop immediately with another planting of the same crop. Otherwise you risk allowing disease and insects to become better established.

Cold Frames and Hotbeds

If you really get into the spirit of gardening, you may want to start with seed and grow your own tomato, pepper, cabbage, and broccoli plants instead of buying them by the dozen from local garden stores. If you need only a few plants and prefer to start from seed, you can grow them in pots in the house. Or if you want more variety as well as enough for yourself and the neighbors,

Among the rewards for the home gardener is succulent sweet corn from early summer on.

Into odd corners, you can fit hills of winter squash. They're heavy producers.

Strawberries, a favorite crop, should be planted in spring and kept free of weeds.

you can start them outdoors. Cantaloupe and watermelons can be given an early start by planting the seeds in cold frames. The cold frame is a box of wood or concrete blocks and covered with frames of glass or clear plastic. It works as a miniature greenhouse without supplemental heat.

The hotbed, on the other hand, is typically built outdoors over a pit filled with decaying manure to produce heat. You can make the hotbed whatever size you want, or you can construct it to match window sashes available. Such a bed four feet square should be large enough to supply all the plants the average family garden needs. Each plant should have about nine square inches of space. In other words, no seed should be closer than three inches to any other seed.

Start with a pit that is two feet deep and put into it an 18-inch layer of fresh manure mixed with straw. Horse manure and chicken manure are favorites for this job. After this is in place, water it and pack it down, then cover it with six inches of fertile top soil sifted and free of large clods. Compost is excellent for this purpose.

The frame over the pit should slope so water runs off the top. A thermometer installed in the hotbed can tell you when to plant seeds. Wait for the temperature to reach about 85° F. Remember that most seeds must be planted shallow. A hotbed takes daily care to see that it is properly ventilated by propping up the top, which is covered with glass or plastic, on warm days and closing it on cool days to keep temperatures inside at the 65° to 75° F. range. Chances are the growing plants will be too abundant and need to be thinned.

More modern hot beds replace the barnyard manure with electricity. Commercial plant producers favor electric heat because it involves less labor and maintains a more uniform environment promising more uniform plants for sale.

Compost Enriches Gardens

As surely as autumn comes, city home owners line the curbs with large plastic bags stuffed with leaves raked from their lawn. This has always seemed to me to be a great waste. Plastic bags produced from petroleum are hauled off by costly petroleum-burning machines to be dumped into land fills and buried with tons of other cast offs. Even in the city, instead of stuffing leaves into plastic bags, I built a wooden bin for them in a corner of the back yard. Into this bin go all the leaves collected from our lawn plus any leaves that neighbors care to contribute.

If I were a good manager of compost and highly accomplished in the organic tradition of gardening, I would no doubt mix these leaves with other materials, water them periodically, turn them with a pitchfork and thereby convert them more quickly into soft dark humus to enrich the garden soil. But starting with low cost materials and looking at the cost-benefit ratio, I questioned whether or not all the work involved would be worth it. Consequently, I decided in the beginning to allow these waste materials to decay at nature's own speed. Without treatment of any kind, the leaves break down in the compost pile within two to three years, forming organic material that any self-respecting plant should welcome to its root zone. The point is that the art of composting can be adjusted to the whims of the composter and to the supplies of available raw materials. Anyone with a home garden can produce compost for it.

One simple method is sheet composting. Again, leaves can be the raw material. Spread them over the garden, plow them under, and let the natural processes of decay do the rest. The rate of decomposition in this case should be considerably faster than in my pile of leaves because the soil with which the leaves are mixed contains the bacteria needed to bring about the decay.

Gardeners often accomplish the same ends by using sawdust, which is perhaps viewed as a waste material at your nearby saw mill. Some people worry that sawdust causes soil to become acid, but that is less a problem than might be imagined. If your soil is already too acid, add ¾ to 1 pound of ground limestone to each bushel of sawdust. The fact is that sawdust may cause more of a problem through nitrogen deficiency than by causing acidity. The Cooperative Extension Service at the Pennsylvania State University recommends adding 25 pounds of nitrogen per ton of sawdust. For gardeners dealing in smaller quantities, this translates into about 1 pound of nitrate of soda, .8 of a pound of ammonium sulfate, or .5 of a pound of ammonium nitrate to each bushel of dry sawdust. The best system is to apply one half of the nitrogen with the sawdust, the other half during the growing season.

You need not be too critical about the rate of application of sawdust to the soil, but a maximum application in any one year should probably be two inches. Work it into the top six or eight inches of soil. A bushel of sawdust will cover 15 square feet one inch deep. Once you use sawdust on your garden, it is a good idea to keep a critical eye on the growing plants. If they grow sluggishly or have yellowish leaves, they are probably suffering from nitrogen shortage. Spread blood meal or soybean meal along the row beside the plants. Manure can also be used as a source of nitrogen and it offers the added advantage of helping to improve tilth.

While these methods get more organic matter into the soil, the well-managed compost pile still has its place, particularly in rural areas where neighbor reaction is not a problem. People often have an exaggerated idea about compost piles attracting rats or giving off offensive odors. These need not be problems. Topsoil itself is a composting agent where organic materials are broken down by billions of decomposing organisms working constantly. It is said that a teaspoon of soil may contain 5 billion bacteria, 20 million actinomycetes, a million protozoa, and 200 thousand algae and fungi. These micro-organisms crowded into the soil expend unbelievable amounts of energy-reducing organic matter to forms that make it available as plant nutrients. Composting is simply a system of speeding up the process.

It is said that in addition to the hundreds of thousands of home gardeners who make compost, perhaps 10 thousand farmers are using it on commercial-sized farming operations. The future promises higher energy costs, more government restrictions on the use of chemicals for farming, shortages of fertilizers, and a growing feeling among most of us that we should recycle more and waste less. In a study at the Center for Biology of Natural Systems of Washington University at St. Louis, under a National Science Foundation grant, 14 full-time family farming operations, managed by conventional methods, were compared with 14 comparable full-time family operations using organic-farming methods, four each in Illinois and Iowa and two each in Minnesota, Missouri, and Nebraska. The organic farms averaged 429 acres each with 250 acres in crop land while the conventional farms averaged 479 acres with 348 acres in cropland. The organic farms had not used chemicals to any extent in several years. The net return for producing food on these lands was $133 per acre for both kinds of farming operations although the cost of production was $31 per acre for organic farmers and $50 per acre for those using chemicals. In 1975 the organic farmers harvested 74 bushels of corn per acre, which was 20 bushels less than the conventional farmers grew. Significantly, the conventional farmers used 2.3 times more energy per unit of crop produced than the organic farmers did, largely due to heavier application of nitrogen. This factor should be especially important as we go into a time of increasing energy shortages.

All manner of organic materials imaginable can be fed into the composting process, including grass clippings, leaves, sod, straw, manure, mushroom soil, corn stalks, vegetable refuse, weeds, and other easily biodegradable plant materials. The size of your composting operation should hinge on the materials and time available.

Grinding or shredding are keys to faster composting because the smaller materials expose greater surfaces to moisture and organisms. The finer the material going into the compost heap, the quicker the decomposition will be completed. Using ground organic materials, the composting process can actually be completed in three to five days. There are now commercially-available grinders and shredders that cut up compost materials so that they can be reduced to humus within 10 days. Even running your rotary mower back and forth over a pile of green material can chop them into finer pieces, thereby speeding up the composting process.

Most people who make compost contain the material in some kind of bin, usually a square four-sided arrangement of poles or a structure made by stacking up concrete blocks to make walls about four feet high without mortar. Baled hay used on one side permits easy addition and removal of materials. Above-ground structures are less work and generally more satisfactory than pits.

Here is a series of steps recommended by the Cooperative Extension Service of Michigan State University for managing the compost process.

1. Start by spreading a six- or eight-inch deep layer of the organic materials to be composted.
2. Sprinkle this with complete commercial fertilizer such as 5–20–20 or 6–12–12 at the rate of three cups per bushel of compost material. Many organic gardeners frown on this use of chemical fertilizers. In place of this, you can use animal manure mixed with the composting materials plus ⅔ cup of dolomitic limestone per bushel.
3. Water the layer thoroughly with a hose, but not enough to cause run-off.
4. Sprinkle a thin layer of fertile soil over the mixture to introduce bacteria and help hold down odors.
5. Repeat the layering process as long as you have material to compost.
6. New layers can be added at any time the material becomes available.
7. The composting material should be kept moist. But after brief sprinkling during the first three days, it may not be necessary to add additional water.

It's a good idea to speed up the composting process by turning the pile every few days to get oxygen to the bacteria.

Whatever the time and method followed, the end product of a composting operation is a rich humus adding fertility and productivity to the garden. And it is done with waste materials.

The best rule for using compost is to apply it heavily. It can hurt nothing, and an annual layer of one to three inches will bring new life to the average garden. For heavy application it is a good idea to spread the compost, then mix it into the top four inches of soil.

Spread compost around trees from a distance of two or three feet from the trunk outward to a foot beyond the drip line at the end of branches. The compost should then be worked into the top soil layer with cultivator or hand tools.

Pesticides Are Tricky

The umbrella term *pesticides* includes all those agents used for killing insects, fungi, rodents, weeds, molds, and other undesirable organisms. We tend to over-kill when confronted with a pest problem, instead of making a careful analysis of the situation.

No organism is a pest until it causes economic or esthetic damage, or discomfort. Its pest status is a function of its abundance. One mosquito or one dandelion does not ruin a summer. The aim in pest control should be not to wipe out all weeds or insects but to reduce their population levels below that threshold where they can be tolerated. In a broad attack on pests, we often kill other beneficial plants and insects that we need. The pest-control problem, which on occasion *is* a problem, deserves careful study and a deliberate approach. Even the discovery of a swarm of termites in the spring is no cause for alarm. The old house will hang together long enough for you to take corrective steps, which in this case will probably be to call on the services of a professional pest-control agent.

Cleanliness around the farm can help control pests. To keep mosquitoes down, watch for the places that hold stagnant water. Clean out gutters and drains. Piles of wood and trash should be removed.

One biological principle in controlling pests is to grow a wide variety of plants to foster a complex wildlife community. This can help keep any specific pest from becoming over-abundant as they might in a monoculture.

If you have a rat or mouse problem that needs attention, use warfarin.

Still the safest fungicides are to be found among the old reliables, including Bordeaux mixtures.

Herbicides can be a special problem because they are often highly toxic and non-specific. The safest plan is to use all herbicides sparingly and always follow the directions. Use them on individual plants you want to kill rather than spreading them broadly. One potent herbicide that I feel should flatly not be used is the brush killer, 2,4,5-T. Neither should chlordane be applied to lawns. Poison ivy stems cut off close to the ground can be killed with amitrole-T poured carefully on each individual plant or painted on with a small brush.

The safest pesticide for indoor use is the fly swatter. Most others found on the store shelves carry some degree of hazard. Find the breeding places and eliminate them instead of waiting to kill heavy infestations of adult flies and mosquitoes. Silica gels and diatomaceous earths will help control such household pests as silverfish, roaches, ants, and fleas.

Suitable insecticides for garden use include Black Leaf 40 or malathion for aphids and scale insects, Sevin for Japanese beetles, cutworms, and chinch bugs.

An old standard home-garden remedy for potato bugs is a bucket and a wooden paddle. My father sent me out many times to "bug the potatoes." The fat bugs are gently knocked off into the bucket in which is a shallow pool of old motor oil.

Organic gardeners take pride in the fact that their cultural methods keep plants so healthly and vigorous that insects and other pests do not attack them seriously. Healthy, fast-growing plants seem to suffer less damage than those under stress.

CHAPTER
17

THE FRUIT ORCHARD

There is a gently sloping grass-covered hill south of our old farm house which seemed the ideal place for an orchard. There was space for enough fruit trees to supply the family needs, the trees would have sunlight, there would be air movement keeping the orchard free of frost pockets, and the hillside was close enough to the house that the trees would not be neglected. The bad news was the soil, thin and infertile. But the same was true for practically all the unforested fields on the place, and I knew that given time, the soil could be enriched.

Our choice of fruit trees leaned heavily to apples. We selected strong young stock of Golden Delicious, Jonathon, and McIntosh, plus Montmorency cherries, Santa Rosa plums, and Elberta peaches. I liked the descriptive writing on the tag attached to the peaches: "Large fruit, with very rich sweet flesh. Free stoned. Leading all purpose peach. Ripens early August. Plant in sunny location." The others had similarly attractive descriptions. In this season, the middle of March, the stock had not started the new year's growth, which is the way it should be when set out.

If nursery stock arrives at an inconvenient time and cannot be planted at once, see that the roots do not dry out. Keep them moist, but not soggy, in sawdust or peat moss and store them in a cool area. If the roots are packed tightly in bundles and the trees must be kept more than a week before planting, it is a good idea to open them up to keep fungus from getting a start on them.

Planting fruit trees is a demanding task. Most full-sized fruit trees should be planted 20 or 25 feet apart while dwarf varieties, depending on the root stock on which they are grafted, can be planted at 10- to 18-foot intervals. A sizable hole must be dug for each tree, one that will permit the roots to spread out comfortably.

The young tree should be planted in a manner that will not injure, cramp, or bruise its roots, including the tiny rootlets. The tree should be planted at about the level at which it grew in the nursery. Take care, however, to see that the graft, especially on dwarf trees, is *above* ground to prevent rooting from this juncture. Into the bottom of the hole goes a mixture of compost and soil on which the roots can rest. Spread the roots out on this bed, and work the soil in among them gradually so that all the areas below as well as above the roots will be filled. I tamp it lightly and carefully as I go and do not exert heavy pressure on it until the hole is well filled and the roots are supported from every direction. What I aim to do is get the roots in firm contact with moisture and nutrient bearing soil so that this replanting will cause minimum stress.

After tamping the soil in place around the newly set tree, water it thoroughly. This helps settle the soil around the root system. Unless there is abundant rainfall, newly planted trees should be watered, especially during their first season. Heavy watering that soaks the soil once a week is better for the tree than more frequent, lighter applications of water.

Ordinarily you will have mixed enough enriching materials with the soil to make more fertilizer unnecessary during the first year. But either commercial fertilizers or organic materials can help guarantee vigorous growth and good health in succeeding years, especially on soils that may be low in fertility. Manure used liberally around the trees should help them grow vigorously. Mulching with manures that are heavy with straw is also a good practice. When such organic materials are not available, commercial fertilizers may have to substitute for them. But if you have an adequate supply of barnyard manure, there should be little need for chemical fertilizers.

If you do apply commercial fertilizers to fruit trees, sodium nitrate or ammonium nitrate will provide the high nitrogen level needed. If a mixed fertilizer is used, it should be at least 10 percent nitrogen. Sodium nitrate applications should be adjusted to the size of the tree, and a quarter pound should be used for each year the tree has been set, with mature trees receiving 4 to 5 pounds. Ammonium nitrate, which contains twice as much nitrogen, should be used at one-half this rate. Broadcast these fertilizers beneath the outer branches in early spring when the buds begin to green.

Young fruit trees, especially if the soil beneath them is covered with a mulch, should be protected from gnawing rodents, particularly mice and rabbits. An aluminum guard, or one made of ¼-inch mesh hardware cloth placed around the trunk and extending some inches below the soil surface where mice might work, will protect the tree. Another material that protects from mice is a layer of cinders. Spread a band of cinders 4 or 5 inches deep around the tree, denying the rodents the cover they would find in a mulch of straw.

Rabbits can be a special threat, and the deeper the snow the higher the rabbit can reach to snip off tender young branches. Where deep snows are common, higher wire guards may be necessary. Deer can also be a serious enemy of new fruit plantings and perhaps the best protection against them are the repellents described in the chapter dealing with wildlife.

If you do not have long practice and experience in fruit culture, the pruning of trees becomes a puzzling necessity. But pruning does stimulate growth, reduce tree size, make spraying and harvesting easier, improve the shape of the tree, and improve fruit quality and production. Here are some general rules to guide home gardeners in the pruning care of fruit trees.

• One year old trees that are unbranched should be cut back at planting time to about 18 inches so that low lateral branches will form. If the young tree is branched when it is set, leave two or three well-placed laterals and remove the others.

Young fruit trees may require a cylinder of wire mesh to protect them from chewing by rabbits.

- Young trees should be pruned very lightly.
- The more mature the tree becomes, the more heavily it should be pruned, especially if it is not growing vigorously.
- The top portion of the tree should be pruned more heavily than the lower part.
- Spring is the time for pruning—early spring when the danger of winter freeze has gone and before the trees begin to bloom.
- Limbs should be cut off at the base flush with the bark because stumps or limbs left at pruning become avenues for disease and insect damage.

• Wound dressing, available at garden and hardware stores, is not necessary unless you are removing limbs larger than two inches in diameter.

• Use sharp cutting tools and make clean, smooth cuts.

• The spraying schedule for fruit trees will vary from area to area, and the soundest practice is to check with your County Agricultural Extension Agent for the most recent recommendations.

• Cherries require the fewest spray applications, followed in order by early peaches and apricots, late peaches and summer apples, plums and pears, fall and winter apples.

Dwarf Fruit Trees

Dwarf fruit trees are popular because they require less space than standard trees. These smaller trees usually range from eight to 20 feet in height, compared with 20 to 30 feet for standard trees. The per-acre fruit yield may be higher for dwarf trees because the total land area is better utilized. Dwarf trees also begin bearing fruit sooner than full-sized trees of the same variety. They are a sound choice if you have limited space for fruit trees, or if you prefer not to invest in ladders and spray equipment needed for working with larger trees. Some dwarf fruits are even grown in baskets and tubs.

Dwarf trees are developed in nurseries by grafting onto different kinds of root stock. It is the root stock that determines the ultimate size of the tree. The size of dwarf for a given variety may vary depending on the root stock, and you should check with the nursery people on the height of tree you can expect from trees you are buying.

Nursery stock will generally be individually tagged with the variety and a key designation that reveals what root stock was used. For example, the tag might read, "McIntosh/M 106." The letters and numbers refer to the root-stock size. Here are some guidelines on various root stocks commonly available.

EM IX.   This stock produces the smallest dwarf tree and can be maintained at heights of 8 to 10 feet. Such trees, because they

A small farm is an ideal site for growing dwarf fruit trees from young stock that comes into production in a few years.

have brittle roots, may need to be supported by a trellis or stake. Good soil is a necessity, and such trees are commonly used either for home fruit plantings or commercially intensive operations.

EM 26. This one also needs support, and the height for which it is usually managed is 10 to 12 feet.

EM VII. Trees growing on this root stock are about half the standard size for the variety, or 12 to 15 feet. They may need some support during the first few years of their lives. Some horticulturists do not recommend this root stock for Red and Golden Delicious apples.

MM 106. This is a fairly rugged root stock and is considered excellent for McIntosh, Cortland, and Spartan, in the 12 to 16 foot height range.

EM II. This is a 14- to 18-foot tree or about two-thirds the standard size. It is a good sturdy root stock, which prospers best on well-drained soils.

MM III. Also producing a tree of 14 to 18 feet, this root stock is considered drought resistant and an early, heavy producer.

Of all these, the most widely used in this country has been the EM IX, earning wide favor among growers of dwarf fruits because of its ability to produce a six- to eight-foot tree when planted in good soil and given proper care. Once in production, such a tree should yield a bushel or more apples a year. The semi-dwarfing stocks, on the other hand, EM VIII and EM II, can be expected to produce 3 bushels or more of apples per year.

Some apple species listed by the U.S.D.A. as well adapted for various parts of the country are: *Northern States*—McIntosh, Northern Spy, Rhode Island Greening, and Wealthy. *Southern and Middle States*—Delicious, Golden Delicious, Stamen Winesap, and Jonathon. *Anywhere*—Lodi, Yellow Transparent, Early McIntosh, and Gravenstein. Of all the dwarf fruit, apples are the ones most widely planted and best understood. But there are other fruits available in dwarf stock.

Pears. Although pears will grow in relatively poor soil, and on sites that may not be well drained, they will prosper better if they are planted on deep, fertile, well-drained clay loam, or sandy clay loam, with a pH of 6.0 to 6.8. Pears should be planted on elevated or rolling land where there is good air drainage to prevent frost damage.

Pear trees are usually self-sterile, making it necessary to plant two or more to assure cross-pollination. With Bartlett and Seckel pears, however, plant another variety to assure pollination.

When the fruit can be lifted and twisted slightly so that it separates easily from the spur, the pear is ripe or at least ripe enough to pick, although it may require some added ripening off the tree. If so, pears should be kept chilled at 35 to 40° F in high relative humidity air of 60 to 70 percent until ripened. In a few days they will reach their maximum quality and texture. Pears store well at temperatures of 30 to 32° F, and some varieties can be kept at these temperatures for several months before they are taken out to ripen.

Fire blight is a problem with pears, and some pear varieties are more resistant than others. If you want to plant them east of the Rocky Mountains and are searching for a fire blight resistant variety, try Magness, Moonglow, Seckel, or Waite. The always popular Bartlett is one of those highly susceptible to fire blight, but may do satisfactorily where spring weather is cool. West of the Rocky Mountains popular pear varieties among dwarf tree fanciers are Anjou, Bartlett, and Bosc.

Apricots. Moongold, Reeves, and Sungold.

Sour Cherries. Many fruit growers list their first choice as Montmorency, a large, flavorful, tart cherry. Other popular varieties include Early Richmond, Suda, and Meteor.

Plums. Among the popular varieties are Greengage, Stanley, Damson and Burbank Purple. It is always a good plan to check with local fruit growers or nurseries to be sure you are selecting varieties suited to your climate.

Trees for People and Squirrels

Nut trees, I always thought, must be easy to grow. In the hills at home we gathered hickory nuts, hazelnuts, and walnuts, and there was no work involved except picking up nuts that had fallen from the wild trees. Looking back, this seemed like all fun and no work. We even had a favorite spreading chestnut tree that for many years beyond its time escaped the blight that within this century, swept through the eastern part of the country killing chestnut trees. You may still find American chestnut trees near the edge of their former range, but in most places the blight attacks them before they are mature and kills them. The one old enough to produce seed is rare indeed.

A naturalist friend of mine has such a tree that, on occasion, bears a limited number of chestnuts, and one year he gave me six of the nuts for planting. One of them is still a thriving seedling around which I built a wire cage to keep browsing animals from

Production, Tree Life, and Start of Bearing of Various Fruit Trees

Fruit Tree	Years from planting to bearing	Useful life in years	Estimated production per tree at		
			3 years	6 years	10 years
APPLES					
Dwarf	2 to 4	10 to 15	0 to 2 pecks	1 to 2 bushels	2 to 5 bushels
Semidwarf	3 to 4	15 to 20	0 to 2 pecks	1 to 3 bushels	4 to 10 bushels
Spur type	3 to 4	15 to 20	0 to 2 pecks	1 to 3 bushels	4 to 10 bushels
Standard	4 to 6	15 to 20	None	0 to 2 bushels	5 to 15 bushels
APRICOT					
Standard	3 to 5	15 to 20	0 to 1 peck	1 to 2 bushels	2 to 4 bushels
NECTARINE					
Standard	2 to 3	10 to 15	1 to 2 pecks	1 to 3 bushels	3 to 5 bushels
PEACH					
Dwarf	2 to 3	5 to 10	1 to 2 pecks	1 to 2 bushels	1 to 2 bushels
Standard	2 to 3	10 to 15	1 to 2 pecks	1 to 3 bushels	3 to 5 bushels
PEAR					
Dwarf	3 to 4	10 to 15	0 to 2 pecks	1 to 2 bushels	1 to 3 bushels
PLUM					
Standard	3 to 5	15 to 20	0 to 2 pecks	1 to 2 bushels	3 to 5 bushels
SOUR CHERRIES Meteor, North Star, and Suda					
Hardy	2 to 3	10 to 15	0 to 1 peck	1 to 2 pecks	2 to 3 pecks
Standard	3 to 5	15 to 20	0 to 1 peck	2 to 4 pecks	8 to 12 pecks
SWEET CHERRY					
Standard	4 to 7	15 to 20	None	0 to 3 pecks	8 to 16 pecks

Courtesy Agricultural Extension Service
University of Illinois

destroying it. I go often to check on its health. I find
to believe that this may be the sole representative of
within miles through a region where the chestnuts once
much of the forest. A one tree chestnut planting, hov
not produce nuts because the chestnut is self-sterile.

Memories of gathering and storing nuts on autumn days
prompted me to take note of the presence or absence of nut trees
wherever we looked at land. One of the early facts I learned
about the land we did buy was that it had few nut trees other
than some young hickories. But I learned that there is an association of nut-tree growers in our state. Your state may have one
also, and the people in your state forestry department can guide
you to its members. There is also the Northern Nut Growers Association, 4518 Holston Road, Knoxville, Tenn. 37914. State foresters
can tell you if there is a state association of nut growers. Corres-
pondence with the people who must grow nut trees led me to
nurseries that sell nut tree stock. A number of large nurseries
around the country offer nut trees.

That first year in my studies of the nursery catalog I considered
both native and non-native nut trees. With all of these trees, you
must consider their ability to withstand low temperatures. This
trait determines how far north they will grow and in what states
they will prosper. Native nuts are generally more tolerant to cold
than the introduced varieties. The most cold-resistant of all are
butternuts. Next in the order of their cold hardiness are hazelnut,
American chestnut, hickory, and black walnut. Native hazelnuts
are no longer as common as they once were. They prosper best in
open sunlight and in old pastures that have been permitted to
revert to woods. But hazelnuts, or filberts, can be bought from
nurseries, and my earliest order included two of these bushes.

We also ordered two Persian walnuts, commonly known as
English walnuts. Hardy stock descending from the Carpathian
Mountain region of the Ukraine and Poland will withstand rugged
winters as far north as Illinois, Indiana and Ohio, but at these
latitudes they are often subject to damage from late spring frost.
A late frost, after a hard winter, may kill the new leaves back
until the plant fails to recover.

Another factor to consider when you buy nut trees is whether
or not they require cross-pollination. Most varieties of nut trees

require cross-pollination with another variety. Nut trees require some care, including occasional fertilization, if they are to show good growth rates. The rule of thumb on nut trees is to apply about a pound of a complete fertilizer such as 12–12–12 per inch of trunk diameter at breast height every spring for the first three to five years. The fertilizer is best applied by putting it into holes in the earth, beneath the branches of the tree. Use a crow bar to make the fertilizer holes, and sink them 15 to 18 inches deep to feed the roots.

Although insects and disease attack some fruit trees, the greatest enemies are likely to be squirrels. Until hunting season arrives, there is not much that can be done.

Pruning nut trees while they are still young helps give them good shape and strong branch structure. As they grow larger, they will need little pruning except to remove dead wood.

There is nothing to keep you from starting your nut trees from seed. The seed (nuts) must, however, lay dormant, as they would in nature, before they will germinate. The simplest way would be to place them on top of the ground and partially bury them, then cover with a little mulch. But squirrels survive the winter by finding and eating such nuts, and you may need to protect the seed through the cold months of dormancy.

This is done by planting the seed in the fall and covering it with a tin can from which you have totally removed one end. The seed should be buried about two inches deep. The can should have a one-inch hole cut in the remaining end and spotted right over the seed. The can, pushed into the soil around the seed, will protect it from wildlife. Cover the can with straw, but when spring comes remove the mulch. The seedling will grow up through the hole in the top of the can. Use an ordinary can, not an aluminum one. The aluminum will not rust out and free the tree as the ordinary can will. Aluminum would have to be cut away to keep from damaging the seedling.

Another method of breaking the dormancy of nut tree seeds, suggested by the College of Agriculture at the University of Illinois, is to place them in moist peat moss or saw dust in a plastic bag that is fastened shut and store them for two or three months in a refrigerator until planting time. Then they are planted two or three inches deep where you want the trees to grow.

Grapes

Many oldtime country homes still have grape arbors outside the kitchen door. And recently, landowners, especially those coming out from the city, are establishing vineyards for family use. Grapes will grow throughout much of the nation if varieties chosen are adapted to their regions. The frost-free period for American and French hybrid varieties should be from 150 to 180 days. Plantings made on south-facing slopes, or on the south side of windbreaks, may have a special advantage. If the grapes are going to ripen into juicy sweet fruit, they need full sunlight and high temperature. In the northern states, low ground that slopes to the north should not be planted to grapes. Soil on which this fruit does best is a sandy loam, deep, porous and well-drained. It also should have an abundance of humus.

The time to plant grapes is in early spring, as soon as the soil can be prepared. When selecting stock from the nursery, choose well-developed plants that have vigorous, hardy root systems. A spacing of 8 feet between plants is right for grapes, and rows should be 10 feet apart. Set each plant an inch or two deeper than it was in the nursery. But before setting the plants out, trim off

Grapes—for jam, jelly, and wine—are favorites with many an owner of a small farm.

any broken roots and all but one of the most vigorous canes. Dig the hole large enough to spread the roots out comfortably. Into the bottom of the hole goes rich top soil on which the grape roots can rest. More soil is worked around the roots and firmed in place. Once the plant is set, prune it again to leave only two strong buds just above the surface of the soil. Late in the fall or early in the spring, treat each plant to a bushel of manure that has been fortified with super phosphate. Cultivate this into the soil once it has been spread between the rows. If you have no available barnyard manure, substitute 10–10–10 fertilizer applied in the early spring at the rate of a half-pound for each grape plant.

If you are setting out more than a few plants, ground preparation for your new vineyard should begin the year before planting. Eradicate as many of the weeds as possible, fall plow and seed the plot to a winter cover crop, such as rye, at the rate of 2 to 3 bushels per acre, or 2 to 3 pounds for 1,000 square feet. Ten or twelve tons of manure per acre will help get the plot in condition.

That first growing season is the best time to build a trellis for your grapes. Most growers build a trellis by stretching two number 10 galvanized wires tightly between strong fence posts spaced at 16-foot intervals.

Grapes should be pruned in early March, or as soon as weather permits, and they should be cut back severely enough that only a single upright trunk with four lateral branches remains. Each of the four young branches selected to be supported by the two wires of the trellis should be left with 6 to 10 buds, depending on the age and vigor of the vines. Some varieties of grapes are less hardy and should be pruned in the fall instead.

With annual attention to pruning, fertilization, and weed control, your grape planting should begin producing in the third year. It will probably survive longer than the weekend farmer who plants it. Vineyards may be a century old and still produce.

Blueberries

Tart, juicy blueberries are among the finer fruits. An increasing number of home gardeners have been planting them, nurturing them successfully, and outwitting the birds who are at least as fond of blueberries as people are. Although this fruit requires careful attention, it is not considered difficult to grow.

People frequently have the mistaken idea that blueberries grow best planted in boggy land, too wet and acid for anything else. But this is a misconception. Blueberries do their best on loose, moist, well-drained soils that are high in organic matter. According to Wisconsin Extension Specialists, "the best soils are sand or peat with a water table at about 18 inches below the surface." Acid soil is an essential, so much so that when blueberries are planted on alkaline soils, the site must first be treated to bring the pH level down to 4.0 to 5.2. The materials used for this are aluminum sulfate or sulfur. For example, if you have a loam soil where you intend to plant blueberries and it shows a pH level of 6.0, you will first need to add 3.5 pounds of sulfur per 100 square feet. This would be the equivalent of 21 pounds of aluminum sulfate. You can reduce the pH one point by working one pound of sulfur into the top six inches of a 100-square-foot area if the soil is sandy. For loam soils you will need to use three or four pounds of sulfur to do the same job.

When choosing the site for blueberries, keep in mind that they are frequently the victim of early frost. For this reason, plant where there is good air flow, not in low areas that might collect pockets of frost. Blueberries also need full sunlight.

If you are setting out a few plants for home use, create a special bed for them. In the site selected for each plant remove about three bushels of soil, leaving a hole 15 inches deep and 24 inches wide. Into this hole goes a mixture made of two parts well-rotted sawdust, leaf mold, or peat, and one part loam soil. Add one-half cup sulfur. Set the plants so that the top roots are three to four inches beneath the surface. Pack the soil firmly around the roots. Finally, mulch the planting with four to six inches of sawdust or straw. This mulch is important to blueberries because it helps maintain uniform soil moisture and holds down soil temperatures in the summer. You may have to replace the mulch from time to time because it is biodegradable.

The blueberries will need fertilizer every year. To begin with, give each plant two tablespoons of ammonium sulfate two to four weeks after planting. Spread it on top of the soil around the plant. Every spring, plants should get two to four tablespoons of a

5–10–5 fertilizer at the season when the blossoms begin to appear. A month later the plant will need two tablespoons of ammonium sulfate. These amounts will have to be increased as the plants grow older and larger.

Do not expect fruit the first year, and do not expect much of it the second year. But nurture the plants properly and prune them modestly. In a few years the reward will be fresh blueberry pie made from home-grown fruit. But do not count your blueberries until you are inside the house with them. Remember the avian raiders. The best way to protect a producing blueberry bush from the birds is to surround it with tobacco cloth or cheese cloth, which can be removed a couple of times a week for the harvesting.

Disease has not been a problem in small blueberry plantings.

Bramble Fruits

Raspberries and blackberries are easily grown in small plantings for family use. Both are at their best in temperate climates. Bramble fruits do not ordinarily do well in the plains or mountain states where summers are hot and dry and winter temperatures may be extremely low. Varieties (now called cultivars) of these fruits have been developed for various geographic areas. The best plan is to check with local nurseries or your county agricultural extension agent before making a choice.

Some parts of your farm may be better than others for growing blackberries or raspberries. They need abundant sun and moisture. Hillsides are better than low areas where water stands after heavy rains. These berries will grow in a wide variety of soils but should not be planted on highly sandy soils. A sandy loam soil on an open, gently sloping hillside where there will be abundant moisture during the fruiting season could be exactly the spot for your raspberries and blackberries.

From one to two dozen blackberry or raspberry plants should supply the average family. If you want them to grow into a hedge, set them two feet apart. But if you set more than one row, leave 10 feet between rows. Otherwise you may have a solid bramble patch. When you don't want a hedge, normal spacing is 8 to 10 feet apart in the row.

Trellises are a good idea and, considering the long life of bramble fruits, can be a sound investment. These supports are essential for growing trailing blackberries or dewberries. But some gardeners also use them for erect varieties. Trellises are made by stretching wire between posts set no more than 20 feet apart. Erect blackberries can use a single wire stretched 30 inches above the ground. The trailing blackberries will need two wires: one at about three feet high, the other at five feet. It is a good idea to treat the posts against decay so they will last many years.

Blackberries and raspberries should be planted as early in the spring as the ground can be prepared. In the south this means late winter, and in the north very early spring. It is a sound practice to work the soil up first as thoroughly as if it were to be a garden. Plow the soil to a depth of nine inches, and then disk and harrow it. One good idea is to enrich the organic matter in the soil first by plowing under a green manure crop of rye or fetch.

If the plants must be held over for planting, keep the roots moist. If they seem to be dry, soak them in water for several hours before you plant them. I'm a firm believer in mudding the roots of plants in a soupy mixture of soil and water before setting them. This brings soil and moisture in contact with even the smallest rootlets.

To set a blackberry or raspberry plant, make a slit in the soil with a shovel or spade, then slip the plant into this space and remove the shovel. Set the plant at the same depth it grew in the nursery and firm the soil around the newly set plant with your foot. Newly set plants may need watering if the season is dry. Thorough watering every week or so is better than frequent, light watering.

Much of the pruning of bramble fruits is a matter of removing dead or diseased canes. And the best time for this is right after the berries have been harvested. If you want to limit the height of your canes, tip prune them back to 36 inches to get a denser growth of lateral shoots.

When you set out your new plants, sprinkle two-thirds cup of

10–10–10 fertilizer in an 18-inch circle around each one. In June give them one-third cup of ammonium nitrate or three-quarters cup of 10–10–10 over the same 18-inch circle. This treatment should get the plants off to a fine first year start. The second year, give them 1½ cups of 10–10–10 over a 30-inch circle, and another two cups over the same area after the harvest and pruning. Thereafter give each plant an annual application of 10–10–10 over a four-foot circle around it in the very early spring and the second application of 1½ cups of ammonium nitrate over the same area after the harvest and pruning. If you are growing your bramble fruits in a solid hedge row, treat each plant to one half cup of 10–10–10 every year after they mature, giving them two-thirds of this plant food in a spring feeding, the other third after the harvest.

Your home planting of bramble fruits should begin to bear in the second summer. By the third summer, these berries should be in full production.

CHAPTER

18

MONEY FROM THE

WOODS

People who buy farm properties often want woods on part or all of their land. Although they may want trees just because they like the woods, they also know that a good stand of timber can have a substantial cash value. More than half of this country's forests are in private ownership, and about 59 percent of the 300 million acres of potentially productive forest land is held by private, non-industrial owners. In the eastern part of the United States three-fourths of the forest land is in small, privately-owned holdings. Whether your farm woods is an acre on a bay along the East Coast, 60 acres of rolling woodlands in southern Indiana, or 40 acres in northern Wisconsin, you may have timber of commercial value.

Most of us, however, expect a woods to do more than grow commercial timber. This is a place where wild things live and where we follow trails to see the spring flowers or to feel the coolness on hot summer days. None of these benefits have dollar values, but they are still benefits, and they're part of the reason why many people want farms.

Cutting trees is not necessarily bad for all wildlife. Some wildlife, including grouse and deer, find more food and cover in the lands that have started to grow back to a mixture of young trees than they do in the mature forests with its widely spaced giants. A long-range forest-management plan may enable you to harvest some of your trees and space out the cuttings so you have woodlands of varying stages of development. A good forester will probably tell you that you can have both wildlife and a timber-management plan.

A woodlot of almost any size may have commercially valuable trees. Most of us must face the fact that we do not know enough to make a sound decision on what to do with the trees, and it may be costly to ask for bids on the timber without some prior advice from a forester. Some professional foresters are employed for the express purpose of giving farmers free help on the management of their woodlands and the sale of their timber. This grew out of the Cooperative Forest Management Act of 1950, which provided for the Federal government to give funds to the states so the state forestry agencies could hire Service Foresters. Typically, one of these professionals is assigned a group of three or four counties where land owners call on him for help and advice. His services may range from cruising your woods and computing the potential yield from trees ready for harvest, to working out a complete long-range management plan for the forest. While working on this chapter, I stopped in the Jackson, Ohio, office of Frank Toth, a Service Forester, who works a four-county area of southern Ohio. He is not a desk-bound forester. He wears field clothes, and more often than not he can be found deep in the woods identifying trees and determining the best thing the owner could do to have his trees turn a profit.

Most farm owners calling on Frank's service are interested first in knowing whether or not they have saleable timber and how best to get it to market. One of his primary duties is identifying the valuable trees and marking those ready for harvest. He can estimate the volume in board feet of lumber to be cut from these trees. The forester usually marks, with a spot of paint on the trunks, the trees that are ready for harvest. This mark will last two or three years, and it is there to guide the timber buyer who comes to cut and haul the trees away. Usually the trees standing on the property line, or very close to it, are spared. He may also leave seed trees to keep young trees coming on.

Even before he begins marking the trees for cutting, Frank

talks with the owner to see what kind of program he wants. While some foresters have professional tunnel vision oriented toward maximum production in board feet of timber with little concern for other forest uses, Frank insists that, where the owner wishes, the forest can be managed for wildlife and recreation, as well as timber. In such cases he leaves occasional old trees, even dead ones, for the woodpeckers. If you want these trees left, get this point across early when talking with your forester. The general tendency among professionals is to clean out any plants not likely to turn a profit in timber.

In addition to marking trees, the forester can give information on how to sell the timber for its full value. He can supply you with a sample contract between owner and the timber purchaser. No timber sale should ever be made without a written contract.

He can also point you toward a purchaser for your timber. Frank keeps a list of 25 to 30 bidders who are always scouring the countryside searching for timber they can buy and cut for the market.

Logging operators can leave a woods in a condition that upsets the owner's digestion every time he sees it. At best, a logging operation is no beauty treatment. The logger's heavy equipment can uproot or break off small trees and leave tire marks that turn to gullies.

The operator will probably need to clear off landing areas to which the logs are skidded for loading. These may be half-acre patches at the rate of about one for every eight or ten acres of woods. Operators like to hold skidding to distances of less than a quarter mile. The routes the operator follows driving the skidder, which is a heavy tractor on giant wheels, can make considerable difference in how the area will recover. With care, the operator can follow the routes least subject to erosion. But logging is a highly competitive business. Some operators are inclined to get in, get the most valuable trees in the shortest possible time, and get out with maximum profit, sometimes at the expense of the land. There is no system of licensing loggers to protect property owners. You must choose with care and understand that some are less inclined to be conservationists than others are.

You will want to get bids from several logging operators. A comparison, however, of the prices they offer is not all you need to know. In addition, you will want to determine which one will do the best job and leave your land in the best condition. Begin by asking the forester to give you estimates on the board feet of timber you have of each kind of tree. This can be used to help you make a choice between the logging operators you talk with. A phone call to the local saw mills can tell you the current price being paid per thousand board feet for the kinds of trees you are selling. In this way you know, before discussions with a bidder, the approximate value of what you have for sale. You can make a mistake selling all standing timber the logger can cut from the place, at a lump sum figure. The chances are he has a much better idea than you do of what he can make from the trees and he is not going to hurt himself. This is why those preliminary consultations with a forester are important.

Walk through your woods with those you invite to bid on the timber. Talk over with them the price they can pay, and how they will move the logs. There may be a forest opening that will serve for the landing, so there is no need to clear cut another area for the operation. Find out where the logging roads will go, and try to avoid the steepest places where erosion will be the most severe. As a final step, ask around about the bidders' competence before you make a choice. Others who have employed them, the extension forester, and even the mill operator, may be able to give you references. If possible, visit a woods where the operator has worked. But keep in mind that any logging is likely to leave the area looking less appealing than it was.

The logger gets paid by the mill for the timber he delivers, and the mill issues scales slips, giving the total amount delivered and prices paid. If you are around when the logging is done, you will know how many loads of logs went out of the woods, and the logger should show you the scales slips when he pays you your share.

Once the logging operation is complete, the logs sold, the money collected, and the loggers gone, you may want to move into your woods and do some cleaning up. Normally there is usable wood remaining there, especially if you burn wood for fuel. The loggers take only the lower part of the tree, usually what they can cut in multiples of eight foot logs below the lowest limbs, and this leaves the tops scattered in the woods. Unless something is done with them, they will need many years to decay and rejoin the soil. But a chain saw can cut them into usable firewood, perhaps enough to last for years, or to sell by the cord. You may find a local firewood dealer willing to clean up the tops for the privilege of hauling them off, or you may want to handle this work yourself. In either case it is a good plan to get at the sawing and splitting as soon as possible so the wood can be hauled in and protected from rot, which within a year or two will cut down considerably on its fuel value.

In some areas there is increasing use of wood chippers. These are brought in by the logging operators, especially if the woods is large. The tops are all fed into the chipper and the chips trucked off to be sold for pulpwood, leaving little to go to waste. This possibility might be worth investigating if you are planning a timber cut.

Much of Frank Toth's time is spent working out long-range forest-management plans for farmers. These may be 20-year plans, aimed at keeping the area productive over the long haul. He will recommend where trees should be planted, where to get planting stock, how to plant the trees and care for the new plantings. His plan will also include recommendations for protecting the woods from grazing, fire, insects, and disease. The forester can help plan forest recreational developments. He can outline timber stand improvement cuts, or as the forester says "TSI." His plan may call for removing the non-economic plants, including wild grape vines, dogwood, and others that promise no income. But the owner may decide to leave these plants for wildlife food producers.

So, if you want to put your forest into a management plan, or are thinking about cutting some of the trees for the market, by all means get professional guidance before calling a timber buyer. The advice the forester gives you could mean a saving of thousands of dollars and make a major difference in the condition of your land after the harvest. You have a number of ways to locate service foresters. One is to write or call your state forestry department in the capital city. Another is to ask your county agricultural extension agent or Soil Conservation Service people.

In some parts of the country there are also private professional foresters who have set themselves up in the consulting business, and who will, for a fee, manage the forest and all the related operations.

Whoever your forester, remember that you will have to live with the results. Your woods may need years to heal after a timber sale, especially a carelessly planned one.

EXAMPLE

TIMBER SALE AGREEMENT

—————, ————————, of ——————————
(I OR WE) (NAME OF PURCHASER) (POST OFFICE) (STATE)
hereinafter called the purchaser, agrees to purchase from

———————— of ——————, ————, hereinafter called
(SELLER'S NAME) (POST OFFICE) (STATE)
the seller, the designated trees from the area described below:

I. Description of the Sale Area:

(STATE)	(COUNTY)	(COMMUNITY)

(BOUNDARIES AND/OR OTHER REFERENCE LANDMARKS)

II. Trees designated for cutting:
   (A) All merchantable timber on the above described tract.
   (B) All ——————— trees which measure ————
        (SPECIES)
        inches or outside the bark at a point not less than 12
        inches above the ground.
   (C) Those timber trees on the above described area which
        are marked with paint spots, one spot on the stump
        at/or near ground level and one or more spots on the
        main trunk of the tree.

III. Condition of the sale:
   (A) The Purchaser agrees to the following:
        1. To pay the seller $————, in lump sum in ad-
           vance of cutting for the above described timber
           products.
        2. To waive all claims to the above described timber
           unless it is cut and removed on or before ————.
           (DATE)

3. To protect from fire and unnecessary injury young growth and other trees not included in the sale.

4. To repair damages caused by logging to fences, bridges, roads, fields and/or other improvements damaged beyond ordinary wear and tear to a state or condition equal to or better than that now existing.

5. Not to reassign this agreement and/or contract without the written consent of the seller.

(B) The Seller agrees to the following:

1. To guarantee title to the forest products covered by this agreement and/or contract and to defend it against all claims at his expense.

2. To grant the freedom of entry and right-of-way to the purchaser and his employees on and across the area covered by this agreement.

(C) 1. Failure on the part of either party, herein mentioned, to fulfill any of these contractual agreements will be sufficient cause to terminate this contract.

2. In case of dispute over terms of this contract, final decision shall rest with an arbitration board of three (3) persons. Each of the contracting parties will select one person and the two selected will choose a third to form this board.

Signed this _____ day of _____, 19_____.

Witnesses:

                                    PURCHASER

_____   _____

_____   SELLER

                                    _____

Black Walnut

Black walnut is the regal tree of the eastern forest, a premium tree worth hundreds of dollars if it is large, straight and sound. Some years ago one company bought a giant black walnut tree from which they were to take a log 37 inches in diameter and 48 feet long, a tree more than 100 years old, at a price of $12,600. More recently, a walnut tree in Ohio sold for $30,000. A price of $500 is not unusual for a walnut tree with a log of veneer quality. There are not many giant old walnut trees remaining because we have over-harvested them for decades. Today we are still cutting quality walnut lumber much faster than we can grow it.

For these reasons owners of walnut trees worry about their safety. Rustlers slip in with chain saws, cut the trees, and leave only the sawdust. What has made this such a valuable wood is not only its dark chocolate color but also its physical nature— straight-grained, strong, hard and heavy, but easily worked with tools. Big uses for walnut are gunstocks and veneer for furniture.

Understandably, farmers ask why this wouldn't be a profitable crop to grow. The answer is that it would be, provided your farm is in the right geographic location, you have the suitable place for walnut trees, and you want to do the work required to raise quality trees.

The best section of the country for black walnut covers Ohio, Kentucky, Indiana, Illinois, Iowa, and Missouri and adjoining parts of several surrounding states. But if your farm lies within this area, you may still not have suitable planting sites for black walnut. Walnuts grow naturally on the beaches along streams where the soil is deep, fertile, and well drained. The soil should have a dark brown color down to 24 inches or so. Hard clay soils or soils that are gravelly are not good for walnut. Often you will find suitable locations in forest openings on north and east facing slopes where red oak, white ash, sugar maple, and perhaps other walnut trees grow. Walnut seedlings need sunlight to get started.

Starting a black walnut planting calls for more than simply sticking the nuts in the ground and sitting back to wait. Weeds compete with the seedlings and must be controlled until the seedlings are a few years old. The U.S. Department of Agriculture, always quick to recommend chemicals, says that herbicides work better and are cheaper than plowing and disking to keep weeds down.

For best survival and growth, the stock you plant should be adapted to similar climatic conditions, and for this reason, foresters suggest that it come from within 150 miles north or south of your farm. Some state nurseries may have seedlings available, or you can buy them from commercial nurseries. Seedlings will probably come as one-year-old trees and should be 10 to 14 inches high and have a stem diameter at ground level of at least one-quarter inch.

Plant late enough in the spring that the ground will not heave from frost. Set each seedling in a hole 10 inches wide and 10 to 12 inches deep so the roots are not crowded. Set them at the depth they grew in the nursery. The holes can be hand dug, but if you can do this work with a tractor-mounted post-hole auger you can save hours of heavy labor. The spacing should be 14 by 14 feet, but you can utilize irregularly shaped spaces for walnut trees where the soil is suitable and the seedlings will not be shaded by other trees.

Pruning the trees early in life will help produce clear butt logs of the required minimum eight foot length. Walnut growers usually aim at trees that have two logs, a total of 17 feet, allowing room for cutting and squaring the ends.

This is a long range crop, one often planted by fathers for their children. But within 30 years the seedlings should have matured into commercially marketable trees that will command high prices, especially if they are large enough and free enough of defects to qualify as veneer stock.

Maple Syrup

The Indian tribes knew how to tap maple trees in late winter and turn the sap to syrup. Maple syrup was among the earliest products sold on the market by early settlers. Most commercial maple syrup production occurs in parts of Ohio and in the northeastern part of the United States. New York and Vermont are famous for maple products. In these areas, or anywhere if you own maple trees, you may want to produce this fine natural sweet for your table and offer the surplus for sale.

The maples with highest sugar content in the sap are black maple and sugar maple. Tapping of the trees should be completed between the middle of February and the early part of March. The farther north you are, the later the sap will run within that period. Trees less than 10 inches in diameter at four feet above the ground should not be tapped. If your trees are the proper size, tap them by drilling a $\frac{7}{16}$- or $\frac{1}{2}$-inch hole three inches deep between two and four feet above the ground. A metal spout is then driven lightly into each hole. Time was when every spout was equipped with a bucket into which the flowing sap dripped. If buckets are used, they should be equipped with a cover to keep out rain water, dirt, and flying squirrels. In recent years plastic bags have replaced buckets, and some operators run plastic lines directly from the trees to central collection points.

In a normal season, a healthy maple tree may yield 10 to 12 gallons of sap. The amount varies, and the rate of flow depends on weather. Sap can be stored for a few days in cold weather, but the sooner it is boiled down, the better your chances of turning out high-quality syrup.

Maple sap is turned to syrup as heat drives off liquids through evaporation. You can expect to use 43 gallons of sap for each gallon of high-quality syrup. The syrup is brought to a boil in a large shallow pan, and the heat is carefully controlled to avoid burning or scorching. As evaporation continues, new supplies of sap are added until gradually the sap in the pan becomes highly concentrated. You should have a thermometer calibrated at least 15 degrees above the boiling point of water because as the sap thickens, its boiling point rises. Special care is needed now to keep the syrup from overheating and burning. When the boiling point of the liquid reaches 7 degrees above the boiling point of water, the process is completed.

Then, filter the syrup while it is still hot to remove crystals and particles from it, and put it into cans while it is still at least 180° F to keep it from spoiling during storage.

You may find it cheaper to buy a gallon of the syrup from the neighbor or from a shipper in Vermont, but syrup from your own trees has a special satisfying flavor when served up on hot pancakes in the farm kitchen.

CHAPTER

19

RAISING CHRISTMAS TREES

Visions of father going into the snowy hills to cut a wild pine for the family Christmas tree are the stuff of which memories and Currier & Ives prints are made. A growing percentage of the conifers gracing American homes today are commercially grown as farm crops, and owners of rural land often consider Christmas trees a possible profit-maker on their newly acquired land.

Americans decorate 30 million Christmas trees a year. Supplying this market is a brand of farming that can be fitted even to small farms from one acre up with a minimum of capital outlay. Successful Georgia tree farmers figure that they can grow marketable Christmas trees in 4 to 6 years, and sell them at about 4 times the cost of production. Planting an acre calls for 1210 trees if they are at six-foot intervals.

But before becoming deeply involved in this enterprise, you should seek advice from the County Agricultural Extension Agent, neighboring tree farmers, and perhaps from the state association of Christmas tree growers.

They can tell you, for example, which species of trees sell best in your region. While Georgia growers sell white pines, Virginia pine, Scotch pine, and eastern red cedar, their counterparts in the Pacific Northwest specialize in Douglas fir. Both may grow Scotch pine, which was originally a European import.

Whatever the species chosen, the aim is the same: to produce a marketable, well-shaped, five- to eight-foot tree in the least number of years.

But before plunging into the tree business, consider the type of soil on your farm. Most species used for Christmas trees do best on well-drained soils that have not lost all their humus to erosion, and that are neither highly alkaline nor very acid.

Also consider labor requirements. Growing Christmas trees calls for more work than you might think. Plantations must be cultivated, cleared of weeds, pruned, and protected from wild animals and tree poachers. Then finally, there is the harvesting. If the trees are planted even with each other in evenly spaced rows, problem weeds and grass in the check-rowed planting are more easily controlled with tractors and mowers. Weeds are a serious problem. They limit light available to the trees, compete for moisture and nutrients, distort tree shape, and reduce rate of growth or even kill trees.

Many Christmas-tree farmers use fertilizer to stimulate tree growth and speed the time from planting to market. Fertilizer should be limited to what the trees need. Otherwise it is wasted and stimulates weed growth. A soil test in advance of planting is important. If the pH is below 6.0, the land should be limed to correct the high acid condition.

Pruning Christmas trees controls their natural growth and produces denser, better-shaped plants for the market. Pruning, usually an early summer job, should aim at developing one main stem, controlling the height of the tree, increasing its density, and giving it an overall more uniform shape.

Trees in a plantation may not all reach marketable size the same year. But in the spaces where trees are harvested, new seedlings can be planted. After the fourth or fifth year, the plantation can be kept in continuous production. Whether or not trees yield a profit after figuring labor, land, and other production costs may vary from one operation to the next, depending on the manager's skill, suitability of the land, and the system of marketing.

There are various ways to sell Christmas trees. Some trees are packed and trucked to distant cities. Others are sold to families who like to cut their own trees. Some farmers do their own harvesting, then sell their Christmas trees at roadside stands.

Here is one sour note out of keeping with the spirit of the season: the more accessible your plantation, the more trees will be stolen. Look again at the location of your land. If it is far back in the boonies, hidden from the public eye, it could be just the place for a flourishing Christmas tree plantation.

This owner of a small farm follows the ancient tradition of cutting the family Christmas tree on his own land and carrying it in fresh. Another possibility is to raise Christmas trees for profit.

CHAPTER
20
LIVESTOCK FOR THE SMALL FARM

The Milk Cow

Landowners who feel that a farm is not a farm without a cow in the barn, should curb the urge to buy a dairy animal until they have considered all the factors under today's conditions. The milk cow is a demanding creature. She must be milked twice a day, Sundays and holidays included. But if you have a tenant who has time and is tied to the place anyhow, or if you want to include the milking and feeding in your own daily chores, the ownership of a cow may be a good investment, especially for a family that needs large amounts of dairy products. A good grade cow can supply 5,000 quarts of milk a year in exchange for her keep. She may also be a pleasure to have around and become something of a pet if she is gentle by nature.

In addition to considering the labor problems, ask yourself some hard questions. Is there an artificial breeding service available in your area? Do you have the pasture and hay for a cow? Does the farm have a comfortable shelter where the cow can be milked and housed? Will there be a use for all that milk? If these questions are answered by "yes," a cow can more than pay for her feed, whether you buy or produce it.

In the course of a year, she is going to consume three to four tons of hay and one to two tons of grain. She will also need a half a ton of straw for bedding. These supplies will probably cost $200 to $300 if purchased.

Obviously you will need pasture for the cow. Two acres of quality pasture will provide for her during the growing season and will reduce feed costs as much as one-half. Mixed grasses and legumes are good choices for pasture over the northern part of the country. In warm southern states, the season for pasturing can be stretched with seedings of crimson clover or small grains.

Among requirements of a milk cow is a generous supply of good water.

Check to learn what pasture crops are best suited to your region.

As winter comes on, the cow must be switched over to good quality hay such as alfalfa, alsike clover, or grass, cut early in the growing season. In addition, she will need a mixture of ground corn and wheat bran along with some soybean oil meal or a commercially prepared concentrate. The U.S. Department of Agriculture says that 100 pounds of hay and 64 pounds of concentrate provide about equal amounts of nutritive value. A medium-size high-producing milk cow will need a daily ration of at least 10 pounds of hay plus a pound of grain for every four pounds of milk yielded. She will also need access to a block of mineralized salt and plenty of clean water at least twice a day.

If a cow seems a sound idea after considering these needs, you are ready to begin scouring the neighborhood in search of the right animal. There are five popular breeds of dairy cattle kept in this country. Jerseys and Guernseys rate high with family farms that keep only one or two animals. These breeds need less feed than the big black and white Holsteins commonly seen on commercial dairy farms. The smaller breeds do not produce as much milk, but their milk is higher in butterfat content than that of the larger breeds.

Pick out a cow, preferably a young one with years of good service ahead of her, that is gentle and easily handled. The size of the udder is not an infallible indicator of milk producing ability. It is a good plan, if possible, to milk the cow before closing the deal to see that she milks easily and is free of bad habits, like trying to kick her keeper out of the stall. How a cow acts is often an indicator of the kind of treatment she has received. Move quietly and gently around her and see if she is well adjusted to people. If she must wear kickers, muzzle, or yoke, look for another cow.

Evidence of mastitis can be detected by drawing the first several streams of milk into a stripping cup, or onto a black cloth stretched across a tin cup, and inspecting it for clots, flakes, blood or strings. In addition, a veterinarian should have inspected her within the previous month for tuberculosis, brucellosis, and leptospirosis.

The cow should always be brushed and the udder washed

before milking to help keep milk clean. The person doing the milking should have dry, clean, well groomed hands.

Raw milk should be pasteurized. Small home pasteurizers are on the market at reasonable prices. Or the milk can be pasteurized by heating and holding it at 142° F for 30 minutes.

Beef for the Table

Many new farmers are convinced they can raise their own beef and perhaps even a few animals for the market. A herd of sleek cattle on a green pasture can add to the pastoral beauty. But a favorite steer may become a family pet, bringing obvious problems at butchering time.

The arguments for raising a beef animal should be economic. Raising a calf to butchering age involves a substantial investment. Cattle should be viewed as a system for converting feed to high-quality beef at bargain prices.

But before you bring home the first beef animal, make certain you are ready for this major step. The most economical gain that you will put on the animal will come from pasture crops. It is going to take at least two acres, and probably more, depending on the quality and productivity of the pasture, to carry one steer through the summer.

Fences are a must. One wire may turn a horse but cattle need substantial fences. A three-strand barbed wire fence will do, provided it's strong fence and the pasture on the other side isn't too enticing. Electric fencing will turn cattle, and it has one added advantage: it can be moved for dividing pastures and rotating the animals to new areas.

A good source of water is essential. Water from brook, pond, spring, or windmill beats any system of transporting it in buckets or tanks.

One system of buying a beef animal—and perhaps the best unless you are an old hand—is to get your calf from a local farmer who maintains a good cow-calf herd. Another source is the local cattle auction, but there you must compete with the regular buyers and will be bidding under pressure. It's a good plan not to go to the auction cold. First, do some advance study of the market by watching local papers, listening to farm reporters on the radio, checking current conditions with a friendly neighboring farmer, and possibly attending a sale or two to get the feel of it before you finally make your purchase.

Most steers are bought in either fall or spring. Calves bought in the fall, if they are good beef or cross-bred animals, are likely to weight about 450 pounds. Prices should be lower in fall than they are in the spring. But if you buy a steer in fall, you'll need hay to feed him through the winter as well as pasture to take him through the following summer. In either case the animal should be ready for butchering the next fall. If you buy a steer in the spring, it will probably weigh 200 pounds more. But you have only six months to feed it before it reaches butchering weight at about 1,000 pounds. Besides, most of the feed that you put into it will be pasture. Either animal, however, will need some grain in the weeks ahead of slaughter to put finish on it.

The best plan is to start with a beef-type animal instead of a steer from a dairy herd. Dairy animals are bred for milk production and as a rule are not as efficient at converting feed to quality beef. The common beef breeds include Black Angus, shorthorn, or whitefaced Hereford. There are also a number of cross-breeding programs that produce excellent fast-gaining beef animals.

In figuring the cost of feeding an animal through the winter you can expect him to consume about 60 bales of hay. If you must buy hay, buy it early. As winter wears on, hay prices go up.

Most small farm operators who keep a beef animal for their own use, have the butchering done at a local slaughter house. They are well equipped for the task and can hang and cure the carcass properly. They can also approach the job without personal attachment to the steer.

Depending on the size of your farm, and the amount of pasture and feed available, you may want to keep more than enough beef for your own family use and gradually build up a cow-calf herd that will provide feeder calves for the market and a source of farm income. Get some counseling from your county agricultural agent and, if possible, from nearby farmers. Remember that there will be years of hard winters or droughts that could

Beef animals or young dairy stock can be sheltered and fed in simple structures.

increase the costs of keeping cattle. One friend of mine had a herd of a dozen fine white-faced cows until the record cold winter of 1976–77. "I had to buy $2500 worth of hay," he said. "I'm selling the cattle off and getting out."

Raise a Buffalo

One evening in Kalispell, Montana, I met Marvin R. Kaschke, and the conversation turned to buffalo, as bison are commonly referred to. Marvin was manager of the National Bison Range nearby, where the United States government is trying to preserve bison, the shaggy, all-American grazers.

"If I were going into farming or ranching today," he said, "instead of cattle I'd raise buffalo. They bring higher prices than cattle," he added, "and they harvest their own hay." There is a steady demand for the meat, and all indicators are that this demand is increasing.

Once there were probably 40 million of these animals roaming the grasslands of America. But the buffalo had to go. Beginning about 1830, the buffalo herds were attacked, and forty years later their numbers were down to perhaps 5 million. Along old western trails, where once millions of buffalo traveled regularly, only stragglers wandered. The greatest herds of grazers the world had ever known were vanishing before the guns that often killed for the robes and tongues alone. By 1900, in all of North America, there were no more than 300 buffalo, most of them in Canada. Finally, when only about 20 wild buffalo remained in the depths of Yellowstone National Park, steps were taken to save them. Already there were a few in private herds, and 21 of these animals were bought up to strengthen the Yellowstone herd. Today this herd, still wild and free-roaming in Yellowstone National Park, numbers about 800 animals.

But now there are buffalo elsewhere, both on private lands and in government herds, perhaps a total of 35,000 across North America. This quantity seems to assure the buffalo a secure future even though all of these animals together would have been lost in one of the herds that formerly grazed the grasslands. Chances are good that these numbers will continue to increase somewhat as farmers and ranchers expand their bison herds.

Buffalo herds are maintained today on four national wildlife refuge areas. These herds must be limited to what their ranges will support, and consequently there is an annual surplus. These animals are sold. From these sales, as well as sales from private herd owners, come the stock for starting new herds. The new owners, in addition to raising animals of commercial value, know the feeling that comes from working with animals linked so closely to the history of the land.

Surplus bison are usually sold at 18 months of age, by age and sex group, through sealed bids. In one recent year's sales, the prices ranged up to $800 an animal and averaged $567.06, with mature bulls bringing the top prices.

But before bringing a buffalo home, be sure your pastures are prepared to hold it. These are powerful animals, and sometimes excitable. Mature bulls will average 1600 pounds. Strong fences are an absolute necessity. The minimum, according to such experienced buffalo managers as Marvin Kaschke, is a fence made of

47-inch woven wire (Style #1047-6-11 or #1047-6-9) set 10 inches above ground level and extending to the top of seven-foot heavy-duty posts, spaced not more than a rod apart. Ordinarily the animals are not likely to test such a fence. Do not use barbed wire. It causes cuts and infections and will not even turn buffalo.

The buffalo, although it will reproduce in captivity and can be managed as a farm or ranch herd, has never fully resigned from the wild. Present-day animals are still possessed of the traits of their ancestors. They are not to be trusted, and even though the animals may seem to be gentle, they bear watching because they can become excited.

One of the beauties of raising these animals is that they will usually range through the winter without supplemental feeding— a capability acquired through ages of evolutionary adaptation to living wild on the plains. If they should need supplemental feeding in severe winters, hay and concentrates normally fed to cattle will be eaten readily. Feed the amount that you would offer cattle of similar weights.

The calving season for buffalo comes in spring, and the reddish brown calves weigh 30 to 70 pounds at birth. Within their first year they should attain weights of 400 to 500 pounds or more. By the time they are two years old, they may weigh as much as 1100 pounds. Cows usually begin mating as two year olds and thereafter have a calf a year, perhaps for 20 years or more. Cows 26 years old have been known to raise strong healthy calves. The gestation period is 270 to 280 days.

Animals butchered for the market are usually one to four years old. They dress out more than 50 percent of their live weight. Buffalo owners usually expect two- and three-year-olds to yield the greatest returns on the investment when sold for meat.

There have been many experiments in crossing buffalo with cattle to produce "cattalo," but for most owners these hybrids have not returned profits as great as they might expect from the pure-blooded buffalo.

Buffalo owners have their own organization, and anybody interested in raising these animals might write National Buffalo Association, P. O. Box 995, Pierre, South Dakota 57501.

The following national wildlife refuges are sources of stock:

Fort Niobrara National Wildlife Refuge
Hidden Timber Star Route
Valentine, Nebraska 69201

National Bison Range
Moiese, Montana 59824

Sullys Hill National Game Preserve
Box 159-D
Devils Lake, North Dakota 58301

Wichita Mountains Wildlife Refuge
Box 448
Cache, Oklahoma 73527

Goats

An ancient proverb, Persian, I believe, says, "If you think you have trouble, buy a goat." But one Persian's trouble may be another's pleasure. Some people find good reasons for keeping one or two nannies around the farm.

First is the milk—pure white, nutritious, naturally homogenized, easily digested, and especially suitable for the young and those unable to digest cow's milk easily. A good nanny will yield a minimum two quarts of milk daily during a lactation period that lasts as long as 10 months. A goat is also good for keeping weeds and briars out of fields. They readily consume the vegetation cows leave behind. A frisky goat, if allowed freedom, is adept at such tricks as climbing to the top of a shiny new automobile and sliding down the windshield, bouncing into the porch swing and down again leaving it clattering against the house, or pulling clothes off the line.

Good fences, at least four feet high, are needed to hold the healthy goat. A goat also requires a dry, draft-free, and well-ventilated shed. You will need a milking platform on which the goat stands with her head locked in a stanchion while being milked.

The breed of goat chosen is not so important as the individual. All the common breeds—Nubian, American, La Mancha, Saanen, Toggenburg, and French Alpine—are good producers. The secret of choosing the right animal is to find the best goat breeders in your region, visit them, ask questions and buy either a good-producing doe or young stock from a good line. The mother should have produced at least 1500 pounds of milk in her last production period. One good plan is to buy two female kids because they can be bred at about nine months of age or when they weigh 75 pounds, whichever comes first. The herd from which they come should be certified free of tuberculosis and brucellosis.

The first half of the year, January to July, is the time young goats are most readily available.

There are goat-breeding associations in many parts of the country and your county agricultural agent can tell you if there is an association in your region. The advantage of relying on an artificial breeding service is elimination of the need to maintain a buck for only a few does, thereby cutting costs. Kids are born from 145 to 151 days after breeding, and the doe generally has two kids. About six or eight weeks before a doe is due to give birth, she should be dried up by discontinuing milking.

The cost of feeding a goat for a year runs about one-sixth the cost of feeding a dairy cow, and feed for goats can be similar to that fed dairy cows. In winter, when the animal is not on pasture, a producing milk goat will need about two pounds of quality clover or alfalfa hay, plus 1½ pounds of silage, and one to two pounds of a grain mixture concentrate daily. The grain mixture may be bran, oats, and a protein supplement, such as linseed meal.

Goats can make good use of root crops. They eat turnips, beets, carrots, and parsnips. These vegetables can be substituted for silage.

If goats are on pasture, the grass provides the roughage. But they will still need grain mixtures if they are producing milk. The amounts of grain, however, for goats on pasture, may be reduced somewhat.

In addition, these animals will need a mineral supplement. They should have access to rock salt all the time. If the hay is not quality legume, the supplement should provide additional calcium and phosphorus. It is a good plan to feed pregnant nannies the hay free-choice, so they get all they want when they want it.

Attention to sanitation is essential around milking goats and the milking area. Milking is a twice daily operation, and the milk is filtered at once, cooled, and stored in the refrigerator. If produced for home consumption, it is commonly not pasteurized.

Sheep

Sheep are an easy challenge for the small farmer and adaptable to a part-time enterprise. Besides, a small flock of ewes can provide two cash crops, lambs and wool, both of which can be marketed in quantities of any size. Pasture alone will produce choice market-grade lambs, provided the pasture is of good quality. But the lambs will also make profitable use of some supplemental grain.

Sheep are ordinarily not hard to handle. But if they ever escape and you have to drive them out of the neighbor's fields, you may ask yourself why you ever bought the first ewe. They do not drive easily; they cannot be forced. For this reason perhaps the most important factor of all for anyone considering a flock of sheep is whether or not he has fences that will keep the sheep in while keeping free-running dogs and other sheep killers out. Without adequate fences you are better off without sheep.

A dog-proof fence should be a combination of barbed wire and woven wire. One good design starts with a strand of tightly stretched barbed wire at ground level. Top this with a 36-inch high fence of woven wire with a 4-inch mesh. Add to this two more strands of barbed wire. Some sheepmen bend the bottom 6 inches of the net wire fence 90 degrees, then bury it in the ground a few inches and weight it down with rocks. Good fences for sheep are especially important between your place and your neighbors'. Elsewhere electric fences can be used, if your sheep are trained to them while they are in short fleece.

In addition, you will need a good source of water. And each ewe will need 12 square feet of floor space in a barn or shed.

Forty ewes may seem to be a large number in the beginning, but this is known as a one-man flock. The farmer who wants to start with a smaller herd of ewes might arrange to share a ram with a neighbor.

If you want to know what's required to keep a flock of 40 ewes for a year, the following list is published by the Agricultural Extension Service, Michigan State University.

10 tons of legume hay
3,000 pounds of grain
10 acres good pasture
1 ram (can be used 5 to 6 years)
60 feet of feed rack space
500 square feet of floor space in a shed or shelter. If lambs are born in May, no shelter, only a windbreak is needed
1 2-ounce drenching syringe
1 salt box
500 pounds of trace mineralized salt
1 pound pruning shears to trim feet
1 pair of good hand sheep shears for trimming wool around eyes and rear quarters
12 lightweight, hinged gates, 4-feet long and 30-inches high, for lambing pens
2 250-watt heat lamps and heavy duty extension cord
3 3-foot by 8-foot gates to aid in sorting and handling sheep

One sound way to start in the sheep business is to buy young ewes and breed them in time for the first lambs to come when the ewes are about two years old. The gestation period is 145 days. Lambs should come in the winter months when cold weather cuts down problems from parasites.

A good season to start in the sheep business is late summer or early fall. More good ewes are likely to be on the market then. A dual purpose breed, developed for both wool and lamb production, is generally the soundest choice.

During the breeding season, the flock ram should be turned in with the ewes only at night. Research has shown that, in hot weather, the rate of conception improves if the ram can be kept in a cool area during the day. Keep a record of the breeding dates for your ewes so that you will know when lambing time approaches because this is a period when the flock will need close attention.

During lambing season the successful herdsman often spends nights in the shed with his flock. He is there to render assistance if the ewes have trouble. Individual lambing pens for ewes in labor are important. So are heat lamps for the ewe and her lambs until the new lamb is dry and nursing. The ewe and lamb should be kept in the lambing pen for two or three days until the lambs have a good start.

Mature sheep, not on pasture, can live well on high-quality alfalfa or clover hay. The sheep will need supplemental grains for four weeks before lambing and six weeks after. The grain supplement can be unground corn and oats, or feed stores can supply complete pelleted feeds. Even lambs as young as 10 days old can start eating hay and grain. It should be offered in a creep feeder, allowing lambs but not ewes to reach it. In cold weather a heat lamp placed over the creep feeder will be an added attraction to the small lambs.

By the time lambs are ten days old, they should be castrated and have their tails docked. At this age these operations cause little shock or bleeding.

Before starting a ewe flock, it is a good plan to stop at the County Agricultural Agent's office and pick up copies of any bulletins he might have on raising sheep. It is also a good idea to talk with successful sheep men or with your veterinarian about the health and care of your flock.

Hogs

Butchering day was always a favorite time at home. At the end of this cold November day, a long table held hams, shoulders, bacon, freshly packed link sausages, and other assorted cuts.

Hog raising can still be a sound part of the small farm scene. Raising swine, even in small numbers, seems to be one of the few farm enterprises that can be profitable in smaller units. The small operator raising hogs can maintain a level of efficiency difficult to attain when a hog operation goes big time.

The small hog operation can provide cheaper meat for the family as well as supplemental income. If you raise more hogs than you need, they can be sold to neighbors, or hauled to market by a local livestock dealer.

Hogs grow rapidly. From the age of eight weeks, when a weanling weighs 35 pounds, the animal should reach a butchering weight of 225 pounds in four months. At that weight the hog should yield 150 pounds of meat in a variety of cuts, along with 25 pounds of lard.

Hogs are most profitable for operators raising their own feed instead of buying commercial rations. From the time of weaning to when hogs are market size, a hog will consume about 600 pounds of grain and concentrate for an average of about five pounds a day. The best grain is yellow corn. Other suitable grains include barley, wheat, oats, and sorghum. In addition, the hog needs a protein supplement, purchased from the local feed store, and a mineral mixture of steamed bonemeal, ground limestone, and salt. The mineral mixture should be free fed from a self-feeder so it is constantly available.

Hogs need a constant supply of clean water. When possible, arrange a watering pan equipped with a float valve to eliminate any need for you to carry water.

Good pasture can reduce feed costs by 10 to 15 percent. Alfalfa, clover, and various grasses, depending on the ones that do best in the area, provide good swine pasture. An acre of pasture will supply six or seven sows.

Hogs are usually weaned in spring or fall, and these are the best times to buy them. The safest place to buy pigs is from a commercial producer with a large, efficient, successful operation. Your county agricultural agent can point you toward hog farmers in the area. It is important to buy pigs that have been raised on clean ground and have been vaccinated against hog cholera.

For butchering, select castrated male pigs. If you want to raise a litter of pigs, it is a good plan to start with a young sow in her first pregnancy, a "gilt," as the hog men say. Or if you raise your own gilt to maturity, she should be ready for breeding at eight months of age. Thereafter she should present you with a litter of pigs twice a year. Keeping a boar to service only a few sows is costly and troublesome and a far easier plan is to haul the sows to a neighboring hog farm for breeding. For bigger litters and more

A brood sow may well fit into your picture of the ideal small farm.

efficient feed conversion, a cross-breeding program is better than raising pure breeds. Yorkshire, Durocs, and Hampshires are favorite breeds, so if you start with a sow of one breed, cross her with a boar of another. Gestation is normally 112 to 115 days.

The farrowing house should be ready for the sow three days ahead of the time she is due to have young. The farrowing house should be scrubbed with hot water and lye and furnished with bedding. It is good policy to feed the sow away from her farrowing pen for the safety of the small pigs. A major source of loss in young pigs can come from the sow stepping or lying on her young. A barn or shed can be converted to a hog farrowing facility if it can be kept warm, draft free and ventilated for winter farrowing.

If you are keeping only one or two sows, quarters can be arranged for them on most farms. Good planning calls for keeping them some distance from the house, because a hog operation can create odors, especially in hot weather.

In summer, hogs need shade. Trees offer natural shade, but where there are no trees, there should be a simple shelter made of poles holding a roof of metal or brush.

A fence that looks formidable to a man is not necessarily going to stop a hog, especially a hungry one. Check your fence situation before bringing home a hog.

Chicken Flock

At one time, a farm without its resident flock of chickens, wandering freely over lawn and barnyard, was not a farm at all. The old hen and her biddies were part of the rural scene.

But more recently, commercial egg and broiler producers have mechanized to reduce labor and feed costs and produce poultry products at a slender profit margin. Economically, these big operators are hard for the small farmer to compete with.

But profit may not be the sole motivation. Some people enjoy having a flock of chickens. They also want fresh eggs and chemical-free meat. For these chicken admirers, a small flock can be a satisfying enterprise, if you have time to give the chickens the daily care they need.

The basic way to start a flock is to buy day-old chicks and start them beneath a brooder. Select a breed suited to your purpose. White leghorn crosses are noted for their egg production. But a good dual purpose breed will be a better choice if you want to produce both eggs and meat for home use. Hatcheries today sell sexed chicks, making it possible to raise a flock of pullets if you want only eggs, or cockerels if you want only friers. With a dual purpose breed you may dress out some broiler-friers at 7 to 9 weeks of age, and roasters at 12 to 15 weeks. If you buy unsexed chicks, you can hold out the pullets for egg production.

Baby chicks need close attention. They can be brooded under a 250-watt heat lamp, one lamp per 50 chicks. Two lamps are better than one, in case one lamp fails.

Chicks are fed chick-starter mash, available from the feed store. At the age of 6 to 8 weeks, begin adding small amounts of growing mash to the starter mash. Increase the proportion until they are shifted completely to this new feed. Chickens at this age also need grain, but it is easier to rely on commercially mixed feeds than to mix whole or ground grains yourself. Pullets should begin laying at 20 to 26 weeks of age, depending on the breed. A couple of weeks before laying they should be switched to a diet of laying mash with grain.

In addition, chickens need grit and oyster shell (calcium for egg shell production) if these are not included in the commercially prepared feed.

Depending on the breed of chickens raised, each producing hen can be expected to consume 85 to 115 pounds of feed a year. In exchange, she should produce 200 to 240 eggs.

This float-equipped watering pan reduces the amount of time you need to spend in caring for poultry.

Simple housing is adequate for chickens. But the shelter must be dry, draft free, and able to be ventilated. One nest box, or a square foot of community nest space, is needed for each hen in the laying flock. Roosts are not essential. Fenced space for the flock is a better management practice than permitting chickens to roam freely. Your yard stays cleaner, and predators are less of a problem.

Chickens are subject to a variety of diseases. If any of the birds stop eating or show signs of sickness or droopiness, quick action is called for. Separate these birds from the flock. Get advice on how to treat the illness, and destroy and burn the birds that become hopelessly ill. Disease prevention programs include keeping waterers and feeders clean, an annual disinfection of the chicken house, and either keeping clean litter on the floor or using a deep litter that can be stirred frequently. Keep the flock healthy and you should never have a shortage of country-fresh eggs.

Keeping Turkeys

A turkey dinner may be delicious, but I've always looked upon turkeys as problem animals on the farm. They are skittish, unpredictable, unintelligent, and disease-prone. Few professional turkey growers would argue these points. But the fact remains that, for some small farm operators, there may be a place for a flock of turkeys, either for sale or for home use.

Turkeys demand considerable area. They should not range on land used for turkeys or chickens within the three previous years. Neither should they roam the farm grounds in the company of chickens. Old turkeys may endanger young turkeys if they are kept together, because of the ease with which turkeys pick up diseases such as blackhead.

Very young turkeys, newly arrived from the hatchery or incubator, should be fed 28 percent protein starter mash for the first eight weeks. Then they are changed gradually onto a growing mash of 20 to 22 percent protein which comes in either pelleted or loose form and should be kept available to the birds all the time.

The smaller breeds of turkeys are ready for butchering as roasters at 22 to 24 weeks of age; the larger types two to four weeks later. Sixteen weeks may be ample to bring the smaller-type white turkeys to roaster-fryer weights.

Open-range rearing of turkeys works best if you have sufficient area to move the birds onto clean ground every few weeks. For the first eight weeks of their lives, however, the turkey poults must be raised in a brooder house allowing one to one and one-half square feet of floor space per bird. Start them out on clean sand, and begin adding straw to the litter after two weeks. If the birds are to be kept in pens until they reach marketing age, they will need five square feet of floor space each. Windows should be screened against sparrows because they can carry disease, and against predators that might panic the skittish turkeys and make them crowd into corners of the house, smothering those on the bottom of the pile.

Turkeys raised on wire are less likely to get diseases. This knock-down shelter can be taken apart and stored when it's not in use.

Ducks and Geese

A flock of ducks and geese can be attractive around the place, especially if you have a pond where they can loaf and swim. For most small farmers, these waterfowl are more a decorative hobby bird than a commercial enterprise. They can, however, provide meat for the family table and occasionally for the market while the eggs that are not kept to produce more birds can sometimes be sold at good prices to a local hatchery.

Geese, of which the two most popular breeds are Embden and Toulouse, can be raised in practically every part of the country. They are strong birds with powerful wings and bills and are usually highly capable of protecting themselves from predators. For most of the year, especially when there is good pasture for them, they require little care or attention. A three foot high woven-wire fence is all that is needed to keep them in their grazing area. Depending on the size of the birds and the condition of the pasture, an acre of clover and grasses will support 20 to 40 geese. Even goslings in their first week of life will eat fresh green clippings carried to them from the lawn. By the time they are five or six weeks old, they can get most of their food by grazing.

Geese are not well-adapted to confinement rearing. These are hardy creatures that will not require shelter except in severe winter weather.

For starting goslings, however, you will need a small area in a dry building, well-ventilated but free of drafts. The floor should be covered with several inches of shavings and the young birds warmed with a heat lamp. Hover-type brooders built for chickens can be used for goslings if they are raised high enough to accommodate the birds. A brooding hen can accommodate four to six goose eggs. An incubating goose can cover a dozen eggs. Young goslings should be protected from the rain while in the down stage, but they can be put out on pasture as young as five or six weeks of age. Chick starter mash can be fed to goslings.

Ducks are important human food. In America, 10 million ducks go to market annually. Most of these come from large, specialized operations which market ducklings at seven to eight weeks of age. There is, however, the possibility that the small farm operator can maintain a profitable flock of ducks if he can find local markets for them.

The commercial duck industry relies on the Pekin. But ducks of this breed seldom raise a brood of their own. So other breeds, especially the Rouen, are more in favor with small farm operators. Flocks of ducks on small farms are often kept for ornamental reasons and may include ducks of various sizes and colors.

Laying flocks of ducks can be left outdoors during the day because most duck eggs are produced at night. This routine simplifies the housing problem. All that's needed if you want to collect the eggs indoors is a small one-story rat-free building with clean dry litter on the floor.

One way to start a flock is to buy eggs from a local farmer and hatch them in standard chicken incubators. Most breeds of ducks require 28 days for the incubation period. An easier, small-scale method is to hatch a brood of ducklings under a broody hen.

The simplest way to feed ducklings is to buy a pelleted ration from your local feed store. It should be available to the birds all the time. Ducks are hardy birds. You are not likely to have the disease troubles with them that are common with chickens. This is especially true if the arrival of the ducklings can be timed so they are outdoors when the new green crops provide them with forage.

Guinea Fowl

One bird that has changed little in the several hundred years since its ancestors departed the acacia thickets of Africa is the guinea fowl. Some people claim this is a pity. I am not recommending that you install a flock of guinea fowl on your country property, nor do I advise against it. I remain neutral. Guinea fowls, it is said, are better watch dogs than dogs are. Day or night, they are extremely noisy birds. At the least excuse, or with no excuse at all, a small flock of guinea fowl can set up a clatter audible on neighboring farms in every direction. Let a strange dog wander onto your property or a Watkins man stop at the door, and the guinea fowl raise their voices in protest. In these modern times, when rural vandalism is a growing menace, this watch dog quality becomes an asset.

When you have too many guinea fowl, or simply can no longer stand their noise, you may discover that guinea is fine table fare. Prepared when young and tender, this fowl has delicate flesh with a fine flavor. It is comparable to grouse, quail, or pheasant, although the meat is relatively dark.

Actually, guineas have been domesticated for many centuries. Ancient Romans and Greeks raised them for food. The earliest settlers brought them to America. Of the three varieties—pearl, white, and lavender—the pearl and white are considered superior. If you think a little flock of guinea fowl wandering over your country property would add local color, check with nearby hatcheries to see where the young may be available. Or if you can find someone who has a producing flock, you may be able to buy a dozen or two dozen eggs to set under brooding chicken hens. The incubation period for guineas is 26 to 28 days, somewhat longer than it is for chickens. It is a sad reflection on guinea fowl that chickens make better mothers for baby guineas than guinea hens do. The hens are more inclined to keep their foster young out of the tall, wet grass and to bring them home in the evening. With care, you are quite likely to have a substantial farm flock of guineas by the end of a single season.

And in due time you will know whether or not this was a good idea.

Rabbits

Chances are excellent that domestic rabbits will be used increasingly for food in future years. The meat is white, fine-grained, low in fat, and high in protein. Besides, domestic rabbits are easy to raise and handle. Younger members of the family can manage the feeding, watering, and pen cleaning chores.

Investment in rabbit equipment need not be large. The hutches are usually kept outdoors. Rabbits are rugged animals, and much of the pens can be built of wire if they protect the animals from winds and strong drafts. Rabbit hutches are usually about 30 inches above the ground to put them at convenient height for the person taking care of them. Floors are wire mesh, allowing droppings to fall through onto the ground, thereby eliminating daily cleaning. Pens must be equipped with water bowls and feed troughs or bowls. The females will need dark nest boxes, which can be put into the pens a few days before the time for them to have their young.

There are a number of breeds popular among rabbit raisers. New Zealand whites are widely raised. These are medium-weight rabbits of four to six pounds at fryer age, or at two months. Flemish giants grow to sixteen pounds or more. Other common breeds include Chinchillas and Rex.

The easiest way to simplify feeding is to offer them a complete rabbit pellet, manufactured by a major feed producer. Otherwise the rabbits have to be given a diet of roughage, grain, protein supplement, and salt. A salt disk nailed to the inside of the pen gives the rabbits free choice. In addition, rabbits can be fed chemical-free lawn clippings or garden greens.

If you feed your rabbits commercial pellets, you can count on using 400 pounds per year for a doe, and her four litters to weaning size. But those four litters should provide 100 pounds of high-quality meat for either the home freezer or the local market.

21

KEEPING BEES

It's easy to sing the praises of the honeybee, and to do so is altogether fitting because this insect not only pollinates billions of dollars' worth of America's farm crops annually but also produces one hundred million dollars worth of honey and beeswax. Bees may be kept by the farm owner who sees his acreage only on weekends. Although bees must be carefully managed, they do not need daily care. Beekeeping is also appealing because it produces a valuable product at low cost. Besides, bees are fascinating to study, and the cost of starting a few hives is not high.

There are successful beekeepers in every part of the country. If you want to join this fraternity, here is what you will need: a hive where the bees can live and store honey; frames supporting the combs in which honey is stored and where young bees are raised; a smoker to calm the bees; a head net and gloves; and a feeder for providing sugar syrup to hives that need supplemental feeding.

If a bee colony is to prosper and produce a surplus of honey, as well as enough to support the bees through the winter, it must have ample supplies of nectar, pollen, propolis, and water. Nectar goes into the making of honey; pollen becomes bee bread on which young bees are fed. The propolis is a building and repair wax used by the worker bees to mend and waterproof their hive.

Bees gather nectar from whatever flowering plants appeal to them, sometimes flying a five-mile round trip in their search. Important sources of nectar include: alfalfa, aster, buckwheat, citrus fruit, clover, cotton, goldenrod, locust, mesquite, palmetto, sage, sourwood, sweet clover, sumac, willow, and numerous others.

Pollen is just as important as nectar. A healthy colony of bees will use about 100 pounds each year as food for the larvae. In selecting a location for your bee colonies, keep in mind that the following plants are especially good sources of pollen: aster, corn, dandelion, fruit orchards in bloom, goldenrod, grasses, maple, oak, poplar, and willow. In addition, many wild flowers, weeds, shrubs, and ornamentals add to the supply. Bees compete for pollen and nectar, so it's a good idea to locate your colonies at least two and one-half miles away from any large beekeeping operation.

People who have never worked with bees before may hesitate at first because of the fear of being stung. This is less a problem to the experienced beekeeper than you might think. People who have worked with bees for a while learn to move slowly and methodically around them and to treat them gently. They find that bees are easier to handle when the weather is pleasant than on rainy days. They also learn that moderate amounts of smoke from a smoker, directed into the hives through the entrance, will bring the bees under control. It is a good plan to use rubber bands around pants legs at the ankle and around shirtsleeves at the wrist to keep bees from crawling into your clothing. It is also wise to use the bee veil (head net) and gloves. If they feel clumsy, gloves may be dispensed with later as you gain confidence. After a few seasons, most beekeepers become acclimated to bees and build up an immunity to their stings. If a bee stings, the stinger should be scraped out at once with a knife blade or fingernail. Anybody who is highly allergic to bee stings should pass up beekeeping for a less hazardous enterprise.

The beginning beekeeper should start on a small scale and enlarge his operation only as he comes to understand bees, and finds a market for any excess honey produced. The races of bees usually kept in this country are: Italian, (the common favorite), Caucasian, and Carniolan. Two or three colonies make a good start. The best time to begin is in the early spring so the bees will be on hand to work the spring flowering plants. One method is to buy a hive complete with bees from another beekeeper. But there is some danger of introducing disease into your operation, and the hives should be inspected and declared disease-free by the state bee inspector. States commonly have laws requiring that beekeepers register their operation with the state for the control of disease.

Another method of getting started is to buy bees from a bee-supply dealer. These usually come in three-pound packages, and queens can also be bought. Package bees can be used either to start new colonies or strengthen existing colonies in the spring. The hives should be ready for the bees before they are ordered, and the best plan is to buy standard, commercially made hives so parts are interchangeable.

Install the bees in hives away from buildings, paths, or other areas often used by people. In cold climates, hives should be in the sun. In very hot climates, they should have shade.

Spring is a vital time in the bee colony, when beekeepers give their hives special attention. Before the major summer honey flow begins, the colony should be built up to a strong working population and if necessary reinforced with package bees. In the spring also, any empty hives should be cleaned. Take a look at the colonies every week or so during the spring and early summer to see that the bees are getting plenty of food. If their food supply is less than 15 pounds of comb honey per colony, the bees probably need supplemental feeding with sugar syrup made by mixing one and one-half parts sugar to one part of water.

Bees that become too crowded in a colony are likely to swarm. The old queen leaves and takes a large number of the workers with her. You can help prevent swarming by adding new supers to the colony before existing frames are filled with honey.

As the colony goes into the winter, it should have at least 60 pounds of honey, or 10 to 15 frames, to see it through the cold months as food for the bees.

Even though you may have only two or three colonies of bees in the beginning, it is important to keep records on them. This paperwork will tell you in succeeding years the dates you carried out various jobs connected with their care and how the colonies responded. Good records are also important if your honey production goes commercial and you must account for it on your income-tax records.

Part of the pleasure of keeping them is studying honey bees and coming to understand the fascinating complex nature of their way of life. As you get deeper into it, you will want to collect catalogues from bee-supply houses and subscribe to periodicals published for beekeepers.

CHAPTER

22

FISHERMAN'S FARM

I know one Midwest farmer who has several beautiful ponds and considers the largemouth bass they produce a major crop. As fast as he can grow them, he peddles them around the country for stocking private ponds. The fun part comes in filling his orders. Instead of draining ponds or using nets or traps, this fish farmer catches his bass with hook and line and claims this method disturbs them the least of any he could use. On any day that he has orders to fill he can be found sitting quietly in his boat on one of his ponds, casting lures with barbless hooks and slipping the fish quickly into the live well of his boat. But anyone producing game fish for sale should clear his operation first with the state wildlife agency.

Some years ago in southeastern Arkansas, I met another farmer whose specialty was fish, but his favorites were catfish. Catfish are big business in that part of Arkansas, and in the last 15 years the production of channel cats there has grown tremendously. My Arkansas friend, one of the larger producers in his state, raises thousands of pounds of catfish annually in shallow ponds and supplies restaurants throughout a wide area.

Trout farming too, has become a major agricultural enterprise, and as a result fine, plump trout are available in restaurants across the country. It is one thing to raise trout, catfish, or bass as a hobby-size operation and quite another to make the venture succeed commercially. While there is nothing to stop the owner of country property from raising fish for the fun of it, as well as for family food, anyone thinking of going into it commercially should begin with a serious investigation of the whole idea.

The most popular of all farm-pond fish nationwide is the largemouth bass. Specimens like this one provide not only sport but also good eating.

One source of detailed information on the trout business is the Soil Conservation Service. Another might well be your State Department of Agriculture. Trout, which require oxygen-rich water, are frequently produced in raceways with running water rather than in ponds. There is a rule of thumb that says a well-managed trout fishery should produce 10,000 pounds of fish for every 450 gallons of water per minute of flow, provided the water temperature ranges between 50° and 65° F and is of good quality.

This is a highly competitive business. Because trout farming calls for cool water, most trout farming is concentrated in the northern tier of states, the Pacific Northwest, the Rockies and the northeastern states and down through the Appalachians. There is also an area of the Ozarks in southern Missouri and northern Arkansas where trout farming can be profitable.

Trout are raised on pelleted commercially produced foods. You can expect to feed two pounds of pellets to produce a one-pound trout where water temperatures are 50° to 70° F. This process will require 10 to 14 months. Fish grow slower in colder waters.

People who raise trout for the market face a challenge in selling them. Trout farmers relatively close to large population centers can sometimes market their fish through "put-and-take" pay fishing operations. Others raise 8- to 14-inch long trout for the market. Some specialize in operating trout hatcheries and producing fish for other fish farmers.

Catfish are raised primarily for the meat market, although some are sold in certain parts of the country for stocking recreational fishing lakes. The most commonly grown catfish are channel cats, but blue catfish and white catfish are also produced commercially. All are native American fish with good conversion rates for turning feed into meat.

Catfish flourish in warm waters, and they should have water above 70° F for at least four months of the year. A commercial catfish farm needs a lot of area. Soil Conservation Service biologists suggest that the catfish farmer may need 40 surface acres of water plus 10 to 20 acres of land for roads, levees and other facilities. Included would be five one-acre ponds for breeding, rearing, and holding fish, plus five more ponds of perhaps seven acres each where the catfish are raised. Complete protection against flood water is essential, and so are methods for controlling water levels when ponds must be drained. Pesticides can be a problem where agricultural lands drain into fish ponds. Getting into the catfish farming business can be a costly process, even after you have the land, largely because pond construction is expensive.

For most country property owners, raising fish is more suitable as a hobby than a business. If I had always wanted to be a fish farmer and had lucked into just the right property, I would talk with the most successful commercial fish farmers I could find, fisheries biologists in government agencies, potential commercial customers who might provide the outlet for the product, and perhaps my banker. Otherwise I would install a modest number of bass, trout, or catfish, depending on which might be most suitable for my farm pond, and settle back to be a contented amateur.

CHAPTER
23
WANT TO KEEP A HORSE?

Of the eight million Americans who own pleasure horses, many are not prepared to give them proper care. They lodge them in the nearest riding stable where boarding, including housing and feed, is costly. Instead of being able to groom and feed the animal daily, the owner may see his animal only every week or two. As far as the horse knows, somebody else owns it, feeds it, and takes care of its living quarters. It is different with the family keeping its own horses on its own land and experiencing the animal's full-time care.

Visions of owning horses may be a motivating force in buying rural property in the first place, especially in families with teenagers. From the first days of choosing a farm, you may have looked for one with suitable pastures and buildings for a riding horse or two. Then the most important challenge of all remains: the need to pick the right horse. Unless you are already an expert at judging a horse, it is essential to seek out experienced help, perhaps a veterinarian or a neighbor, who really knows horses and what makes the difference between a sound investment and a 1,200-pound mistake. Horse-trading has long been a highly specialized and often risky enterprise.

Locating horses for sale should not be difficult. They are advertised in newspapers and on bulletin boards at local riding stables. Word of mouth can lead you to available horses if you let the word get around that you are in the market. Livestock auctions are another possibility, but this is a poor place to buy a family riding horse, even if you know horses. You usually don't have the opportunity to check an animal thoroughly or investigate its background and habits. This scene, where the action is fast, is best left to expert horse traders.

Before you buy a horse, study the subject well enough to know the common breeds. There are five highly popular breeds of saddle horses. The *Arabian horse* is a sleek-looking intelligent animal, appealing not alone to the desert tribesman who developed them in North Africa and Arabia but also to other owners wherever they are found.

The *Morgan horse* is an American-developed breed, sure-footed, compact, alert, and versatile.

The *quarter horse* came out of the West where it is famed for its high speed on the short track, ruggedness, and the alertness that enables it to cut cattle from a herd or meet the other demands of the working cowboy. It is possessed of an even disposition that does well for the person seeking a horse pleasant to ride and easy to work.

Perhaps the smoothest gait of all saddle horses is possessed by the *Tennessee walking horse.* The walker is normally a strong, calm animal.

The *American Saddle horse* has been especially developed to display style and elegance in the show ring. Most experienced horsemen would advise against purchase of a horse retired from the show ring and suggest instead one that might be less high strung.

Another horse that has come out of the West is the *Appaloosa,* characterized by heavy markings and spotting on the hind quarters. Strong and sure-footed, the Appaloosa can also be a calm animal and one easy to work with.

For younger riders, the best choice may be a pony. Not only will the food bill be slightly lower for a pony, but the animal is better fitted in size to its rider. This can mean more pleasure for the young rider until he outgrows the pony. Ponies are breeds of small horses standing no more than 14.2 hands or 14 hands and 2 inches. A hand, the common measurement used by horse owners, is four inches.

If you are thinking about a horse for the show ring, or raising animals for sale, you may want to consider buying a registered, purebred animal within your chosen breed. The purebred horse, however, can run into a lot of money, perhaps thousands of dollars. For this reason most people buy a good grade animal or crossbred horse and pay from $250 to $750. The factors that help determine the price may be the animal's age, degree of training, and sex; local market demand; and even the season.

"The cheapest and best time to buy a horse," says the University of Illinois College of Agriculture, "may be in the fall because some owners feel that they do not have the time or adequate shelter and feed to carry a horse through the winter." Also at this season you may find a favorite horse being given up by an older teen-ager departing for college. If you buy in the spring, you can expect prices to be somewhat higher for the same horse than it might have been the previous fall because the season of horse shows and good riding weather is at hand.

No riding horse should be bought in a hurry. Allow time to check the horse, and see how it reacts to you. If possible, ride it. The average horse for most adults should stand 15.0 to 15.2 hands high and weigh from 1,000 to 1,200 pounds. It should not carry a lot of fat nor be so broad in the back that your legs don't hang down comfortably.

"You want a horse with a good disposition," says one of my friends, an expert in buying and working with horses, "a horse that will let you move up to him, quietly lay a hand on his neck, run your hand down his leg and lift a foot without serious objections. If he goes into a corner of his stall, turns his back toward you, and lays his ears back ready to fight you, you know he may have a disposition problem."

So observe its manners. The horse should lead readily with a halter and be willing to load quietly into a horse trailer. It should stand quietly and patiently while being saddled and mounted. If it fights or rears against the saddle or bridle, you would be wise to look for another animal. A well-trained and well-mannered horse responds readily to the bit or reining and does not make its rider tug and pull to give it directions.

Watch carefully when the horse starts off at a walk. If the horse has any lameness, it often shows up before the horse is warmed up. For a comfortable ride, the trot should be smooth and even, not short and choppy. When trotting, the feet should be picked up cleanly without a lot of stumbling and dust-kicking. Also watch the horse canter; check for a jolting stiff-legged stride that will give you an uncomfortable ride. Suspect lameness when the horse continually shifts its weight from one foot to the other. Be especially wary of horses that show such signs as awkward gait, lowered head when walking, difficulty in backing, and legs that do not move in a normal manner.

The inspection process should focus on the horse's natural symmetry and balance. More than just show-ring requirements, these traits indicate how well the horse might be able to carry out its work. Each breed of horse has its own characteristics, and the horse you are considering should show these characteristics. He should have the type, size, and conformation called for in the description of his breed. But there are characteristics of a horse, regardless of the breed, that experienced owners seek. You may hear a few well-established things in horse circles, and they are significant. Included in these are "no feet or legs, no horse", "no top, no price," "no middle, no stamina," and "light muscles, poor power."

If your dealer and your knowledgeable adviser fall into the language of the horseman's world, you may be at a loss to follow their conversations. But you may, with some study beforehand, still check the various features of the horse yourself.

Here are some of the characteristics you should look for:

Inspect the head and neck. The head should not look especially large or small for the animal. Horsemen say that intelligence is indicated by a broad, full forehead with wide space between the eyes. However look with disfavor on a dish-faced or concave-faced animal and also a convex profile or a Roman nose.

A broad, strong, muscled jaw is a desirable feature.

The animal should have bright and clear eyes.

Its nostrils should be large, enabling it to take in the oxygen it will need for full exertion.

Eyes that show a lot of white sometimes indicate a mean-tempered horse.

Horsemen like a horse to have ears of medium size, pointed, and carried up, giving the animal an air of alertness.

The long, slightly arched neck should be lean and muscular.

Take a look at the horse's mouth. Upper incisors hanging over the lower teeth, known as "parrot mouth," is considered an abnormality. The opposite, known as "monkey mouth," is also an undesirable trait. Either condition makes it more difficult for the animal to eat and reduces the value of the horse if you decide to sell it.

Next, consider the animal's forequarters. This includes everything from the feet to the shoulder. The shoulder should be strong and well-muscled, and the sloping lines should blend smoothly with the withers. Pay special attention to the position of the elbows. They should bear the weight of the horse evenly, centering it on a straight line from the center of the feet to the middle of the shoulders. If the elbows are too close together, the horse's front feet may toe out. If they are too far apart he may be pigeon-toed. Also look at the knees from the side. If they bend forward too far, this condition is known as "buck knees"; the opposite "calf knees."

Then take a look at the hindquarters to see that the hips are level and well muscled. According to B. H. Good, author of "The Sound Horse" published by Michigan State University's Cooperative Extension Service, the horse's hocks should receive special attention. "Since the hocks are subject to so much unsoundness (bone spavins, bog spavins, curbs, and thoroughpins)," he says, "good conformation in that region is especially desirable. The hocks should be wide, deep, flat, clean, hard, strong, well-supported, and correctly set. Large, round, thick, meaty, coarse, soft or puffy hocks are not only unsightly, but are subject to unsoundness." There are seven bones in the hock, and swelling is a common sign of unsoundness in this area of the horse's leg.

Also take special note of the horse's breathing. Any kind of noisy breathing is a warning signal. It the animal coughs or seems to have difficulty expelling air from its lungs, or if its abdomen and flanks heave and jerk as it breathes, the condition may be one that cannot be cured. If the horse shows no such symptoms but you want to check further, give it all the water it will drink, then trot it to see if a breathing problem appears.

Good eyesight in the horse is important whether in the show ring or the field. Horses that don't see well may stumble and hesitate. You may be able to tell if a horse is partly blind by moving your hand in front of its eyes to see if it blinks. Cataracts are ordinarily easily detected. Indicators of a partial blindness in a horse include shying at objects, stumbling, and constant moving of the ears as the animal attempts to compensate for its poor sight. Moon blindness (periodic opthalmia) should be suspected if the eye is cloudy, watery, or inflamed. This condition may clear up but later reappear and, in time, could result in total blindness in the affected eye.

A persistent bruise or irritation in the withers, where the front of a saddle rests, may have caused fistulas. These painful swellings heal slowly and may even require surgery.

The indicator that stockmen use to determine a horse's age are its teeth, particularly the six incisors in the front of the lower jaw. The first to appear in a new-born colt are the milk incisors, the center pair, which come in when the animal is about eight days old. These are followed by the laterals, which appear on either side of the milk incisors at the age of about eight weeks. The other pair, on the outside of the laterals, are the corner incisors which the foal gains when about eight months of age. The two teeth in the center, the milk incisors, give way to permanent teeth when the animal is two and one half-years old. If the horse still has its milk incisors, they will be small, white and smooth. The permanent ones, replacing them, are grooved and are considerably larger and more heavily stained.

At the age of about three and one-half years, the horse replaces the lateral incisors with permanent teeth. A year later the corner incisors are replaced with permanent teeth. To the knowledgeable horseman, the degree of wear on the top surface or depression in the top of the permanent incisors becomes an indicator of the horse's age because years of use will grind them smooth. By the time the horse is six years old there may no longer be center cups in the lower incisors. A year later the cups in the lateral incisors may also have disappeared. If the corner incisors have no cups in the surface, the horse is probably more than eight years old. When the horse is past the age of nine, all the lower incisors are worn smooth. To the horseman, he is then "smooth mouthed." This inspection can be carried a step further by checking the upper incisors where the cups of the center teeth are worn smooth by the time the horse is about ten years old. A year later, the upper laterals also have no cups left and by the time the horse is twelve, the cups have disappeared from the upper corner incisors. Beyond the twelve-year period, the age of a horse is largely a guess.

It is good to keep in mind that a horse matures when four to five years old. It is in its prime between the ages of five and twelve. An older horse, however, may be mild-mannered and easy-going and could therefore be an excellent choice for a young or inexperienced rider.

In addition to the horse's physical soundness, the potential buyer should be alert for bad habits the animal may have developed, especially if it has been stabled and not given regular exercise. Chewing of mangers, known among horsemen as "cribbing," may be the result of boredom. So may swaying back and forth in the stall. The horse that practices cribbing may also have occasional colic caused by wind sucking, a condition he will probably get over.

Some animals bolt their grain too fast, a bad habit that horsemen sometimes cure by placing grapefruit-sized stones in the grain box. Obviously you will think twice before buying a horse whose habits include kicking, balking, running away, rearing, unwillingness to stand quietly for grooming or saddling, or showing a general bad temper.

The proper care of a horse will include shoeing. For this work you need an experienced farrier. Having the horse shod is especially important if the horse is worked on hard surfaces because the hoof wall wears away faster than it grows. In addition, shoes improve traction as well as helping give better balance and gait.

Riders with no experience should be given instruction by a skilled rider. There are some basic things the instructor will point out. First, before mounting, check the saddle girth to see that it is tight enough. Some horses have a habit of expanding their bodies with air when being saddled leaving the girth too loose. The horseman should check before mounting and tighten the girth if necessary.

The horse should be mounted from its left side. Gather the reins in your left hand, keeping just enough pressure on the horse's mouth to keep the animal under control but not enough to make him turn or back up. Then, while holding the reins above the horse's neck just in front of the pommel of the saddle, place your left foot in the stirrup. Take a grip on the saddle with your right hand and spring up on your left foot and into the saddle smoothly and quickly while the horse stands quietly. The ball of each foot should rest on the floor of the stirrup. The rider sits squarely in the lowest part of the saddle, picking up the motion of the horse and riding naturally. The reins are held in one hand, ahead of and above the saddle horn. The other hand rides on your thigh. Elbows remain close to the body. The reins need not be held tightly. With western horses particularly, guiding is usually done by neck reining: if one rein is laid against the side of the horse's neck, this is enough to turn him.

Any horseman should practice some basic safety precautions. When you approach a horse speak to him. Do not take him by surprise.

Be quiet, gentle, and friendly around horses, but do exercise immediate firmness with a disobedient animal.

Never lose your temper with a horse or mistreat him.

Be especially careful around stallions.

When leading a horse, do not wrap the strap or rope around your hands or body.

Avoid leading a horse close to other horses.

Leather shoes will help protect your feet to a considerable extent if the horse should step on you.

Do not tie a horse to a wire fence because he might injure himself in the wire.

When tying a horse, use a short rope—not one long enough to entangle him.

Never mount your horse in close quarters or inside a barn that has low ceilings.

Slow down when making sharp turns.

Avoid running horses up and down hills.

There is an old rule saying to walk your horse the first mile and the last. This routine gives the horse an opportunity to loosen up at first, and later to cool down before being stabled. After hard exercise the horse may want a lot of water. Don't let it drink all it wants. Instead make it take a few swallows at a time. A horse should not be fed heavily just before or just after a vigorous workout. After it has been working, the horse should be groomed and rubbed dry.

A large part of the cost of keeping a horse (and a major factor in its welfare) is its feeding. Ordinarily, it is good practice to give a horse as much hay as it will eat. If you are starting a horse on a grain ration, a safe rule of thumb is to allow it a half pound of grain daily for each 100 pounds of body weight. Then it can be worked up to a full ration by increasing the total by one half pound every third day. The total needed will vary with the horse and how hard it is working. Your veterinarian can advise you. Horses on grain should be fed two or three times a day, preferably during the cooler hours in summer. The best choice of grain for a horse is oats. Horses that are not working hard can live well on hay alone. Mixed hay that includes both grasses and legumes is often a good choice for two reasons: 1) it contains a higher level of protein than straight grass hay, and 2) some legume hays, when fed straight, may act as a slight laxative.

The best way to cut feeding costs is to provide good pasture throughout the growing season. Horses can live well on grass. Give mares that are nursing and hard-working some grain in addition to pasture.

Because of convenience, horse owners today often prefer to feed their animals pelleted rations. Feeding ear corn will help keep horses from bolting their grain. Horses not working and not on pasture will eat about two pounds of hay for every 100 pounds of body weight daily.

The keeping of a horse involves weekly chores in which the whole family can participate. Once a week, the stable needs to be cleaned and supplied with fresh bedding. Horses need to be groomed and exercised. But this is the fun part.

Eventually you may develop riding trails on your farm by the judicious clearing of brush and limbs along paths leading to quiet and scenic corners of your holdings. It is on these trails that rider and horse begin to understand each other and enjoy the outing together.

Many people who buy small farms are seeking a place where they can keep one or more horses.

CHAPTER

24

HOW ABOUT A FARM
POND?

Realtors frequently say, "Right there, in that ravine, would be a fine place for a pond. All you'd have to do is throw up a little dam across there." But before you start such a project, remember that the building of a pond is serious business calling for expertise. A "little dam across there" could be a good idea. If you own land and are thinking about building a farm pond, call your local office of the U.S. Soil Conservation Service. Government technicians are paid to assist you in site selection and pond designing.

Even if you do not see a suitable location, you may still have a good place for a pond. On the other hand, a valley might be unsuitable for an impoundment because of the size of its drainage area. The ideal drainage area will vary with the part of the country in which your land lies. In drier areas you may need a larger watershed. Your soil conservationist can help you determine this.

Other features must be considered in choosing a pond site. You must have the kind of soil capable of holding water. Clay soils are usually best because clay particles are small and pack together tightly. Where necessary, however, soils can be treated with Bentonite to help make them impervious to water.

The more of the drainage area there is in woodlands or permanent pasture, the less silting the pond will suffer over the years ahead. Silt that washes into a pond shortens its life. If the runoff comes from cultivated fields and fertilizer washes into the lake, the water is enriched by it. This enrichment speeds up the growth of aquatic plants, including algae, and, through a process called eutrophication, shortens the pond's life expectancy. Any pond will eventually fill up because nothing is static in nature. But the proper choice of the site, and the management of the watershed, will help lengthen the pond's life. If possible three-fourths of the drainage area should be in sod or woodlands. Otherwise the pond can be protected from excessive silting by building a terrace or diversion ditch around the upper side and by contour farming the watershed. Ponds should not be located where barnyards or feed-lots will drain into them.

The pond should probably not be built by damming a creek, even one that runs intermittently. Again your soil conservationist will know what is best.

The location chosen should offer the possibility of fairly deep water. Emergent aquatic vegetation flourishes in shallow water, and a pond too shallow may become so weed-choked that it is good for little except bullfrogs and muskrats.

You can build a pond by making a semi-circular dam on a slope to catch runoff, or by excavating the whole thing. The bigger the dam, the higher the cost. As one soil conservationist states it, "The cost of a pond is the cost of moving dirt."

The common methods of charging for the services of a bulldozer are by the hour or by the cubic foot of earth moved. Some contractors will estimate the cost and quote a figure on the whole job. By taking bids, you can compare costs. Costs often vary widely, depending on the contractors. When it comes to selecting the person to build the pond, you want someone on the job who knows what he is doing and who will give you a fair deal. The best plan is to select a contractor with pond building experience, someone whose past jobs stand as his recommendations, and who takes pride in his work. Inquiring around the neighborhood will help uncover the right person. Talking with others who have recently had ponds built can narrow down the choices.

When planning your pond, give thought to your reasons for wanting it. If it is strictly for stock water, you may get along with less impounded water than you want in a combination pond that also serves as a family swimming and fishing hole or as a source of water for household use or irrigation. Talk with your conservationist about why you want a pond and about the amount of water you need. It may make sense to plan two small ponds instead of a single, large one.

I recently stopped to visit a neighbor who was building a new three-quarter-acre pond. The soil conservationist was there, and

The completed farm pond often becomes a favorite spot for picnics and fishing.

we reviewed points that go into such a construction job. Step one, after the soil conservationist completed his drawings, was to clear all the vegetation and topsoil from the area to be flooded and spread the topsoil above the water line. This step allows for greater water storage capacity.

Large stones and stumps were removed from the dam area. The technicians recommend that the area be cleared 10 feet back from the shoreline.

The next step, and one of the most critical and essential in the dam building, was to construct the core. The core begins as a trench beneath the dam along its entire length. The core becomes protection against water's seeping out beneath the dam under the pressure of the water impounded behind it.

"We did the core wall at least the width of the bulldozer blade," I was told, "and usually wider, because this width gives the operator room to maneuver the machine when he packs clay back into it. The walls of the core trench will slope upward. The trench will be a minimum of three feet deeper than the bottom of the dam and may go considerably deeper depending on local conditions. What the designer wants is a solid base for the core, not deposits of porous sand and gravel, or layers where large boulders are buried.

Once the trench is dug, the clay, usually from the trench itself, is put back into it in layers four to six inches deep and packed tightly by either the bulldozer tracks or a sheepsfoot.

Before the dam is built is also the time to install structures for carrying off the excess water and for running water to stock-watering tanks. My neighbor had already decided to install a concrete watering tank below the dam for his stock.

"You can use a one-and-a-half-inch pipe," the conservationist recommended. "That will be ample. Run it under the base of the dam. For your dam, this will require about 80 feet of pipe. Attach an elbow to the end in the pond, and onto this you put a four- or five-foot upright pipe as an inlet. Cap the top of the inlet pipe off to keep out vegetation and other materials that might clog the water line. Drill a number of holes in the upright to let water in. You won't need a screen around the pipe if it is arranged this way. Then you can run water to the tank by gravity flow and attach a float valve to the lower end of the pipe to turn the water on automatically as the tank level drops."

This arrangement is far better for the pond than allowing stock to wade and drink directly from it. The animals would muddy the pond water and destroy the grass around the pond.

In designing the pond outlet, the Soil Conservation Service follows detailed specifications. Smaller ponds may need only a sodded overflow. For larger watersheds, you may have to install a metal drain pipe beneath the dam. An eight-inch diameter tube can carry off an amazing amount of water. A new one-acre pond down the road from our farm has a 40-acre watershed. It is equipped with a tube beneath the dam. The tube is eight inches in diameter and empties below the dam. The tube inlet establishes the pond's normal pool. Mounted on top of the tube is a baffle plate that the engineers say keeps water from sloshing around as it swirls around the end of the pipe and forces maximum amounts of water into the tube for rapid drainage during storms. This pipe is expected to carry off all the excess except for heavy storms on the average of every two years. For coping with such goose-drowners, the dam has a sodded overflow at one end. It is one and a half feet above the pipe and well below the top of the dam so that even in the heaviest storms, the dam will never "top out." Under no circumstances does a pond owner want water to go over the top of the dam. Such water might cut into the dam and destroy it.

In recent times, regulations have become increasingly strict on the design and approval of new dams, partly because of such disasters as the Teton Dam in Idaho and others that have failed, and partly because of growing populations in downstream valleys. Where homes stand below a dam, the regulations are especially stringent. Do not go ahead with a dam, even a small one, without working through your local SCS people.

Once the dam is completed, it should be seeded as soon as possible to a grass crop that will establish a heavy sod and protect it from erosion. The seeding should cover the lower side of the dam, as well as the top and the space around the pond down to its edges. Again, seek the recommendations of your soil conservationist on the grass varieties to plant. He will probably suggest a heavy grass such as fescue, seeded with a cover crop of oats to

This outlet pipe for a farm pond is eight inches in diameter and is fitted with an attachment that breaks up the normal circular flow of water and thereby increases the pipe's capacity. A sodded auxiliary overflow area handles exceptionally high water.

protect the soil until the grass gets a start. Within a year after the pond is finished, it can look as if it has been a feature of the landscape for years.

You will probably want to plant trees and shrubs around the pond eventually to increase its appeal to wildlife and add to its natural beauty. These plantings are usually not extended close to the dam itself, however, because tree roots penetrate and loosen the earth of the dam and also attract wild animals that may tunnel into the dam. If you buy a place that has a pond, and trees are growing on the dam, clear them off. The best cover for the dam is a heavy sod.

Both state and federal agencies supply fish for stocking farm ponds. Your soil conservationist, your local conservation officer, or your game warden can supply details on how to apply for fish. Sometimes fish must be picked up at the hatchery. Often they are brought by truck to a central distribution point in the area, and people who have applied for them pick up the fish on the appointed day.

Most of the fish supplied by these agencies are largemouth black bass and bluegills (also known as bream in southern states). The bluegills provide both fishing for you and food for the bass. Channel catfish, sometimes stocked with them, are good sport fish and fine eating.

In some northern states with colder water, trout make a good choice for stocking the pond. Three widely used stocking plans are to stock with trout, bass-bluegill, or bass-shiner. Bass and bluegill make for better spring and summer fishing. Fishing in trout ponds is usually better in fall, winter, and spring. Trout need water that stays cool. Usually the pond should be eight feet deep or deeper, and perhaps spring-fed. Such conditions are most likely to exist in northern or western states, and at higher elevations.

If you stock with trout, you will probably have to restock the pond every couple of years. Trout do not reproduce well in ponds and usually survive only three or four years.

Shiners tend to disappear within five or six years and this lack can lead to an over-population of small bass.

Keeping bass and bluegills in the proper ratio to one another is sometimes difficult. When bluegills produce too fast for the bass to consume them, they become stunted. The pond may then have to be drained and restocked.

In northern states, with cooler water and shorter growing seasons, the per-acre production of pond fish is lower than in southern states. Fisheries biologists A. W. Eipper and H. A. Regier, writing in a Cornell University bulletin entitled "Fish Management in New York Farm Ponds," say, "Trout ponds can support annual harvests of about 20 to 40 pounds per acre (depending on the number stocked), and bass-shiner ponds can provide bass harvests averaging about 25 pounds per acre per year. Bass-bluegill populations can support average harvests of about 15 pounds of bass and 35 pounds of bluegills per acre per year."

In Georgia, according to fisheries people, an unfertilized pond should produce up to 40 pounds of bluegills and 10 pounds of bass per surface acre.

In southern states particularly, farm-pond specialists have for years advocated fertilizing ponds to increase their productivity, much as you might fertilize other crops. After its first year of life, the fertilized Georgia pond can be expected to grow about 150 pounds of harvestable bream (600 to 700 fish) and 30 to 35 pounds of harvestable bass (25 to 30 fish) per surface acre.

Productive ponds are most often not those with gin-clear water. The more fertile ponds harbor populations of organisms that keep light from penetrating deeply. These organisms become food for small fish that, in turn, are food for larger fish. Fertilizer stimulates this growth. Your county agricultural agent or Soil Conservation Service technician can help you plan a fertilizing program for your pond.

In addition to fishing, the pond may provide your family with a swimming hole. Larger ponds are sometimes outfitted with a diving platform anchored in deep water. The shores of the pond become a place for family picnics. Some pond owners construct party shelters beside their ponds. You might also want to build a boat dock where you tie up a canoe or fishing boat.

Whatever use you make of your pond, it can add both beauty and value to the property if it's well-situated and properly built and managed. But a farm pond can be costly. Costs vary widely, but building a pond with three-quarters to an acre of surface water might cost $2000. It may be well worth the investment to have the water for livestock, fire protection, irrigation, or just for the fun of it.

The Freezing Pond

You may want to keep part of your pond ice-free, whether for the benefit of ducks and livestock or the protection of overflow structures. I know of one pond that suffered unexpected ice damage during a severe winter. This pond owner did not know until summer that ice had pushed the top eight feet of his concrete vertical outlet two inches off center on its base. Water penetrated the outlet at the break and escaped in such large amounts that by midsummer the pond level had dropped several feet.

The owner considered building a new spillway. Finally, he settled on the simplest answer of all. Drawing the water down to a level below the break, he sealed the broken area by building forms and pouring a band of concrete 8 inches thick around the structure to cover the broken area. There was very little leakage, and his pond filled again with the coming of spring rains.

The next winter the pond owner was determined to keep the ice away from his concrete outlet. His solution was a small submersible pump for which he paid $50. First he attached a 50-foot garden hose to the pump. Then he cut a wooden plug and inserted it in the open end of the hose, tightened a metal clamp on it to hold it in place and sealed the plug in with a rubber based sealer. Next he drilled ⅛-inch holes at 18-inch intervals the full length of the hose.

This pump, with the hose attached, was suspended in the deepest water beside the outlet so that the bottom of the pump was just off the bottom of the pond. The perforated garden hose was laid around the vertical outlet through which water overflows.

When the unit was turned on, the pump brought water bubbling up from the bottom of the lake. Within 24 hours this warmer water had melted the ice for 8 feet around the outlet, and it kept the water open through weeks of sub-zero weather that winter. An inexpensive unit like this can keep an area of the pond open for waterfowl during the winter.

A fringe benefit of having a farm pond is the opportunity to take scenic photographs as the seasons change.

CHAPTER 25

ENCOURAGE FARM

WILDLIFE

The rewards of owning country property include hearing the bobwhite and the whippoorwill, learning where the groundhog lives, and knowing where the red fox has her den. Get two or more owners of country property together, and there is soon talk of the deer one has seen by the edge of the woods, the coyote in the meadow, the ducks that come to the pond, or the pileated woodpeckers that cruise the woodlands. Agricultural colleges have come to recognize this widespread interest in wildlife, and within the agricultural extension service today are wildlife specialists who spend much of their time answering the questions of country people about wildlife on their land. They can tell you how to manage your acres to improve them for everything from cottontail rabbits to yellow warblers. Wildlife may not offer a ready source of cash income, although there are exceptions, but its presence adds an intangible that becomes one of the rewards for buying a small farm.

In the eyes of the ecologist, variety is a key word. The more species of wild animals living together in their complex inter-relationships, the more stable the wild community is. A farm provides an excellent laboratory to observe relationships of animals to their environment, to understand the dependency of an animal on the habitat. Each has its own needs. The woodcock probes the soft earth of swamp thickets for earthworms. The ruffed grouse searches for berries and fruit in forest openings. The bluebird patrols the field borders. And the barn swallow that plasters its mud nest to the beams in the old barn will scoop insects in the yard. Each has its place, and the farm with a wide variety of habitat types promises you wild creatures to match the varied settings. Farms of the past were often rich in wildlife, as they should have been. Because these general farms had livestock including cattle, sheep, hogs, and horses, fields were separated by fences. These fencerows, growing up in brush and weeds, provided thick cover and abundant food. Each such fence became a wildlife refuge. It served as a travel lane of protective cover linking woodlots with open fields and marshes with uplands. No wild animal was far from the food or cover essential to it.

The variety in livestock was matched by the broad spectrum of crops grown. Even the smaller subsistence farms produced corn, wheat, oats, soybeans, and garden crops along with hay and pasture, with each field providing a different biological community.

Too often during those harsh years, wildlife was viewed as the enemy of farmers, sometimes with reason, sometimes not. The fox that slipped into the chicken yard had what today might be called an adverse economic impact. But such events aroused passions often out of proportion to the actual threat. Hawks were always under suspicion. To my father, whether it was the red-tailed hawk searching for rabbits or the marsh hawk winging over the open fields watching for mice, all hawks were "chicken hawks." Those that approached too close, or tarried too long within shotgun range, might be removed from the avifauna. There was a sense of satisfaction in killing the varmint believed to be an enemy of man.

Such an approach to wildlife management had its origin in earlier days when pioneering settlers saw the wilderness as something to be fought and conquered. Down came the bears, wolves, cougars, bobcats, eagles, and any other creature believed to compete. The world of these animals was changed. Some—

especially the large animals with narrow choice of food and low reproductive rates—never recovered. There was no longer room for them. Only in recent times, when there is far less wildlife, have attitudes begun to adjust. Now laws have been passed to protect the wild creatures.

But perhaps the greatest threat to the wildlife of rural America was the changing agricultural pattern. A revolution came to the farms of America. Small farms, no longer economic units capable of competing, were brought together to form larger farms. The results are seen on any drive through good farming country. The variety of crops is no longer there. Corn grows to the horizon in fields chemically treated to keep them free of weeds and insects. Or the one crop may be soybeans, cotton, or wheat. Modern big farming tends toward monoculture to maximize per-acre profits. No longer is there the great variety of habitats for wild animals, except on the small farms that are managed, at least in part, for the pleasure they bring their owners.

There are several reasons why the owners of small farms might look to the welfare of the wildlife on their acres. Some people want to go hunting on their own land. Hunters, and there are 20 million of them, have found increasing difficulty in locating places to hunt in recent years. Big commercial farms not only have little game to offer but also tend to shut out hunters because they interfere with the fast-paced work and, in some cases, threaten livestock and property. Part of the shortage of hunting lands can be traced directly to the burgeoning human population and the expanding subdivisions. So the citizen who still feels the urge to hunt may see the wild game populations as a major reason for buying a country place and a further reason for managing intensively for wildlife production.

For others, simply seeing the wild creatures around the place, or knowing they are there, becomes ample reasons for making the farm as attractive as possible to wildlife. Bird-watching is a rewarding activity for many. At our place we keep a printed bird list inside the door of the old farm house, and whenever we discover a new bird we check it off on the list. Even casual bird-watching can lead to interesting discoveries on a farm almost any month of the year. Equipment needed is simple. A bird book

Time spent on the land brings people close to the wildlife they share it with. These young barn owls endear themselves to the owners by specializing in the extermination of rats.

Although deer generally stay hidden and feed by night, their hoofprints will tell you if they're traveling over your farm.

Some people buy a farm so they'll have a place to hunt game such as this pheasant.

to help in identification is considered essential. Two are especially popular. One is Roger Tory Peterson's *A Field Guide to the Birds* or its companion volume *A Field Guide to Western Birds*. Another one good to have around the country place is *Birds of North America—A Guide to Field Identification* by Chandler S. Robbins, Bertel Bruun, and Herbert S. Zim. Any of these is small enough to be conveniently carried in the field.

In addition, a pair of binoculars becomes a good instrument around the farm, whether you are a bird watcher or not. They can help you tell whether or not the person walking across the back field is a family member, or they can bring you close to the fox den across the valley, as you watch the pups at play on a soft spring day. If there is not already a pair of binoculars in the family, this is a good idea for a Christmas gift. We keep a pair hanging near the kitchen door, and they are used often.

Selecting the pair of binoculars is not as difficult as it might appear at first. There is a difference between binoculars and field glasses. With a field glass, light goes directly through the instrument as it does with a telescope. Field glasses are two small telescopes mounted together. But they have their limitations. They can provide only limited magnification and a narrow field of view.

But binoculars, instead of directing the light straight through to the eye, send the image backward then forward again, using two pairs of prisms critically set at angles to each other. Because of this arrangement, binoculars can give greater magnification and wider field of view in a short and easily carried instrument. The prisms can be jarred out of line if the binoculars are dropped or bumped against a tree or fencepost. With the less expensive brands this is even more of a hazard than it is with the more sturdy costly ones. The best choice is the highest-quality binoculars you can afford of the well-known name brands. Good ones can last a lifetime while inexpensive ones may soon need to be replaced.

Binoculars are described by such combinations of numbers as 8x40 or 7x35. Perhaps the most common of all is the 7x35. The mystery of these numbers can be stripped quickly. The first figure tells the power of magnification. Why then not a 15x or 20x for a really close-up look? The answer is that motion, as well as image is magnified. It's difficult to hold the more powerful instrument. If you have a large pond where you often see ducks, you may want a 10x binoculars or even a 20x scope mounted on a tripod.

That second number gives you the diameter in millimeters of the objective (front) lens, and this dimension is related to the width of the field of view seen through the binoculars. The wider the objective lens, the wider the field of view. The advantage of a wide field of view is that you can more easily locate images and follow action.

Before buying a pair of binoculars, check to see if *all* glass surfaces are coated. Manufacturers normally coat such surfaces with a thin treatment of magnesium fluoride. This coating cuts down the loss of light from internal optical surfaces and reduces glare. Hold the instrument up at an angle toward a fluorescent light. Coated surfaces will look blue or amber. But if you see white spots in these colors, you can assume that there are internal optical surfaces that are not treated.

Photography fans, whether they specialize in landscape, wildlife, or unidentifiable objects, have special reasons for buying a farm of their own. On the land you own, you need ask nobody's permission to set up a photo blind beside the brown thrasher's nest or the gray fox's den. I have a movable canvas blind with an aluminum frame and can set it up quickly when I need it. Your camera can enrich the hours spent on the land, as well as make a permanent record of any farm event from building a fence around the calf lot to catching a big bass from the pond.

Some farm owners like to build trails that lead to interesting natural features, and occasionally they will go so far as to make a nature trail—labeling trees, rocks, and flowers. The arguments against a trail include the possibility that walking the same path time after time could cause erosion. But without trails, some areas of the farm may not be enjoyed—especially if they grow up to brush and dense undergrowth.

A trail does not have to be fancy or surfaced with wood chips. Settle for minimum trails through your property.

The footpath can be narrow. If people hope to see wild creatures along such pathways they should move quietly and in single file. Clearing a trail may call for use of a pair of brush clippers, a machette, or a bush hog behind a tractor. In some areas a once-a-

Children find the countryside and its residents filled with mysteries.

year mowing will keep a trail open through grassy fields or bramble patches along the edge of the woods and fields. The idea is to make maintenance as simple and easy as possible while keeping a trail open enough to be hiked comfortably.

Choosing the route for a foot trail should not be done casually or hurriedly. We have a favorite trail, which has grown gradually since the first time we walked over the place. It meets one of the prime recommendations for a nature trail by leading to a wide variety of vegetation types. From the old farm house it starts out past the garden and along an open ridgetop field with a view down the valley. It goes around the pond where redwings nest in the cattails, and wood ducks sometimes visit. Then, it leads into an oak forest, eventually out into another open field, and finally to a hillside where towering pines shade the ground. Most, but not all of this trail, is gentle walking. It is not marked with ribbons or signs, because these little man-made additions detract from the sense of wildness. But hikers limited to marked trails may miss new discoveries. At the back of our place, I turned away from the line fence one afternoon into the woods and came out on the edge of an exposed sandstone outcropping I had never seen before. This was our discovery of Rocky Hollow. The quiet wooded ravine has become a favorite place.

Trails need not have fancy resting places, but a "sittin' log" here and there can be a good idea. A section of log can be converted to a comfortable and handy bench by sawing a slab off its top with a chain saw. These seats become places not only to rest but also to wait and watch for birds, squirrels, and other wild neighbors that refuse to show themselves until the woods grow quiet and feet are still.

If you know the way well enough to find the sittin' log at night, there are special treats waiting because different players are on the woodland stages. You may spot the owl in flight, or hear the fox's padding feet as he hunts along the trails for a scurrying mouse. And overhead the stars shine brighter than they ever do back in town.

There is, of course, nothing to keep you from developing a more formal nature trail if this is what you want to do. You are free to label the trees and rocks with scientific names and choice

Butterflies flourish in areas where insecticides are not widely used.

bits of nature lore, to cover the trails with woodchips, or to lead visitors by the hand. It's your place.

Attracting More Wildlife

The owner of a farm does not have to settle for the wildlife he finds on the place. Many projects, some of them simple and undemanding, can help increase these wild populations.

For example, deer will travel considerable distances to come to salt. At the village feed store I bought a 50-pound block of salt and put it out on the ridge a hundred yards from the house, where we might see the deer, but close to a hillside thicket into which they could escape if they felt threatened. This proximity to cover keeps the skittish deer feeling more secure.

Instead of leaving the salt block on top of the ground, or setting it on a stake as farmers sometimes do for their cattle, I dug a hole and dropped the block into it so the top of the salt was about even with the top of the ground. Rain melts the salt and carries it into the soil. Within days we were seeing deer tracks around the salt lick.

Nest boxes will help increase populations of many kinds of wildlife. In areas with ample crops of nuts, acorns, and seeds for squirrels, but few old trees with natural nest cavities, some artificial nest boxes can correct the situation. Squirrels need more dens than you might believe: one for the male, another for the female, and later a third for the new litter of young. The female squirrel will usually have two litters of three young each during a season. The recommended size for a gray-squirrel den box is $6\frac{1}{8}$ x $7\frac{5}{8}$ inches inside measurements and 14 inches high. It needs an opening 3 x 4 inches near the top and should be mounted 20 or 30 feet up in a tree at the edge of a woods.

This box may become the home of a pair of screech owls instead, but there is nothing wrong with that either. Screech owls are highly interesting neighbors with an insatiable hunger for small rodents.

If you want to erect homes for other birds around your farm, the following list gives tested dimensions for nest boxes for various species.

Species	Length and width Inches	Depth of cavity Inches	From entrance to floor Inches	Diameter of entrance Inches	Height above ground Feet
Bluebird	5 x 5	8	6	1½	5–10
Chickadee	4 x 4	8–10	6–8	1⅛	6–15
Titmouse	4 x 4	8–10	6–8	1¼	6–15
Nuthatch	4 x 4	8–10	6–8	1¼	12–20
House wren	4 x 4	6–8	1–6	1–1¼	6–10
Carolina wren	4 x 4	6–8	1–6	1½	6–10
Violet-green swallow	5 x 5	6	1–5	1½	10–15
Tree swallow	5 x 5	6	1–5	1½	10–15
Purple martin	6 x 6	6	1	2½	15–20
Prothonotary warbler	6 x 6	6	4	1½	2–4
Crested flycatcher	6 x 6	8–10	6–8	2	8–20
Flicker	7 x 7	16–18	14–16	2½	6–20
Golden-fronted woodpecker	6 x 6	12–15	9–12	2	12–20
Red-headed woodpecker	6 x 6	12–15	9–12	2	12–20
Downy woodpecker	4 x 4	9–12	6–8	1¼	6–20
Hairy woodpecker	6 x 6	12–15	9–12	1½	12–20
Screech owl	8 x 8	12–15	9–12	3	10–30
Saw-whet owl	6 x 6	10–12	8–10	2½	12–20
Barn owl	10 x 18	15–18	4	6	12–18
Sparrow hawk	8 x 8	12–15	9–12	3	10–30
Wood duck	10 x 18	10–24	12–16	4	10–20

Farm owners who have ponds or marshes on their property may be able to attract the most beautiful of all North American waterfowl—the wood duck—by erecting nest boxes. This duck, often found along woodland streams, normally chose a hollow tree for its nest site. If the nest was ideally located, the ducklings could leap from the entrance of the nest cavity directly down into the water.

But modern timbering practices and land clearing seriously reduced available nest cavities for the wood duck. This lack, plus over-shooting, helped bring the wood duck to seriously low numbers early in this century. Then new laws brought them protection, and sportsmen's groups, state agencies, and private land owners began erecting nest boxes for them. The result was a resurgence of wood duck populations. Today they are again abundant, and it is common for pond owners to have pairs of them rearing their young where they can frequently be seen by family members.

Wooden boxes work well for these ducks. Old nail kegs have been used. So have packing boxes of various sizes. But the most commonly erected wood duck nest box is a metal cylinder designed by Illinois waterfowl biologists. Made of 26-gauge metal, such a box can be fashioned into a cylinder with a 12-inch diameter and a depth of 24 inches. A cone-shaped roof made of the same metal is fastened to the top of the cylinder with metal screws. The cylinder's metal bottom is also attached with screws or soldered in place. The 3 x 4-inch entrance hole is cut two inches from the top. Because the young birds may have trouble climbing from this nesting cavity, you should equip the inside of the box with a strip of ⅛-inch or ¼-inch wire mesh up to the entrance hole so the ducklings can get a grip.

This box, with the entrance facing away from shore, should be set on a pole that supports it five feet or more above the water level. A cylindrical predator guard on the post beneath the box will help discourage raccoons and other predators that might try to raid the nest.

The box should be in place early in the spring by March in most areas. Furnish it with a three-inch layer of wood shavings to provide a bed for the clutch of 10 or 12 eggs the female will lay. The larger your pond, the more pairs of wood ducks you may be able to attract. One North Carolina farmer had five occupied boxes on an eight-acre pond.

Winter wildlife shelters not only help wildlife through the roughest months, but also provide your family members an excellent opportunity to watch the winter wildlife show. Winter feeding, however, should not be interrupted once it has begun. Birds become conditioned to relying on the feeding station. Farm owners who get out to the country only on weekends should either not feed the birds or else build feeding stations capable of holding at least a week-long supply.

One way to build a sheltered feeding station is to set four corner posts about 20 inches high and four feet apart. Nail crosspieces on top of the posts and cover the shelter with sheet metal to keep out rain and snow. Then cover it with brush, leaving the sides open so wild animals can come and go easily. This feeding station should be in the open but close to thick natural cover so birds and mammals that use it can escape predators. If it's close to natural cover, your feeding station will draw more wildlife.

Such a feeding station can be equipped with a self-feeder, set under the protective roof, and kept supplied with cracked corn or other grain that moves down to replace grain eaten from the bottom of the feeder.

With or without the added artificial feeding, enough wildlife will survive the winter to start the new crop of young the following spring. Even where deer suffer winter starvation, supplemental feeding seldom does much good for the overall population. The biggest benefits may come to the people who provide the food. This is enough to justify the practice because it gives people more opportunity to see wildlife.

Perhaps the best way to supply food for wildlife is to plant special wildlife food patches. Many kinds of plants have proved suitable for wildlife plantings. State and federal wildlife agencies use them, and so do private nature centers and individual land owners. Often wildlife food can be planted in an odd-shaped corner not suitable for standard farm crops.

The Missouri Department of Conservation says, "Annual food patches of recommended mixtures, located near natural cover, . . . furnish food in late winter months when natural foods are at a minimum."

These food patches need to be protected from livestock if they are to yield food for wildlife. It is good planning, say the wildlife managers, to plant food patches at least a quarter-acre in size. This can best be done by setting aside a half-acre plot and planting one-half of it in alternate years. The half not planted will produce volunteer wild foods, adding to the variety of foods available. Strip planting near good cover is a common method, and a food plant strip 7 yards wide by 180 yards long covers about a quarter acre. Good mixtures for such plantings are dwarf grain sorghums, soybeans, and millet. One mixture commonly used is two pounds each of sorghums and soybeans, and one pound of millet.

Prepare the soil by plowing under 50 pounds of 12–12–12 fertilizer on the quarter acre. Then disk the soil to make a good

If you're a gardener interested in wildlife, plant a few sunflowers for the birds. They'll harvest the seeds during the cold months.

seedbed. After broadcasting the seed, cover it lightly with disk or harrow.

The land around the edge of the woodlot can be especially valuable to wildlife if a 10- or 15-foot wide strip is set aside permanently for these animals and planted with food and cover-producing shrubs and trees. Plant the species that will grow tallest near the woods; plant the lower growing ones on the outer edge. If such strips are left unmoved, unplowed, and ungrazed they will seed by natural methods and grow mixtures of plants that will continue to support wildlife. Or you can speed up the process with the "plow perch" method, usable not only along woodland borders but anywhere you would like to establish a wildlife area.

This system encourages the birds to plant their own favorite food crops. Here is how it works. In late summer or early autumn, plow a strip of land six feet wide where you want the planting to grow. This might be along the edge of a pasture field, but it should not break up a field that you may later want to have in one piece for crop production.

Next, set a row of fence posts down the middle of the newly plowed strip. These should be spaced 20 feet apart. Finally, nail one or two wires to the posts the length of the row. These are for bird perches. During the fruit producing seasons, the birds drop seeds wherever they perch, and the special advantage is that the foods they plant are ones of their own choosing. You can probably boost the rate of production by fertilizing the food patch. If all goes well, the birds should plant such choices as dogwood, blackberries, wild cherries, elderberries, mulberries, and more.

Multiflora rose was once touted as the finest wildlife food plant to come along since the invention of sweet cherries. But, it has disillusioned its champions by growing out of bounds and spreading wildly over pasture fields. Now propagation of this plant is forbidden by law in some places. A vigorous growth of multiflora is considered goat-proof. But avoid it. If you are fortunate enough

Dogwood not only has these attractive spring blossoms but also provides food for wildlife.

to have none on your place when you buy the farm, do not tempt fate.

One of my friends, a widely known wildlife artist, moved to the country several years ago and inherited, along with a fine old farm home, perhaps the most prosperous multiflora-rose planting in the Midwest. An earlier owner had wanted to do something for wildlife. His multiflora plantings flourished and spread so well that today a large percentage of the farm is impenetrable. Whole fields have been taken. When an acquaintance in another state announced that he was going to set out multiflora, my friend found the biggest plant he could, pushed it over with a tractor blade and cut a short section off the stem. The stem was as big around as a man's wrist. He sent the sample to his friend with a note saying, "Here's your dainty little wildlife plant." By return mail he had a note saying there had been a change of plans.

At least one state (Ohio) now has a belated law forbidding the planting of multiflora rose. There is also a campaign to treat plantings with Tordon 10K, a powerful chemical that kills all broad leaved plants on the area, rendering it unsuitable for re-planting for two years. Land owners who buy this chemical are required to take a brief training session in its safe use. It should not be used near water. So far there is no indication of harmful effects on livestock or people. County agricultural agents have the latest information and regulations on it.

One wildlife food plant highly recommended by wildlife man-agers is the autumn olive, or Elaeagnus (*Elaeagnus umbellata*). It's not related to the olive at all but is instead one of a group of plants indigenous to the temperate regions of Europe, Asia, and North America. It has been widely distributed around the world, first coming to this country from Europe in quantity in the 1880s.

We ordered three autumn olive plants the first year we were at Spoon Hollow. Because the directions said the plants would prosper in infertile locations and because I had no trouble finding such places, I set them out with high expectations. I fertilized them and spread some mulch around them. At first they grew slowly, but after a season or two they picked up and flourished.

The leaves are silvery, at least while they are young. The plants grow to heights of 15 feet and branch out thickly. They are heavy producers of reddish fruits. In one New York State test, 24 plants produced 900 pounds of fruit in one season. Although these plants are usually grown for wildlife, the fruit is edible by people and can be used in jelly. Everything from mockingbirds to black ducks eat them. Doves, cedar waxwings, bobwhites and pheasants, as well as squirrels and raccoons, come to the autumn olive for the harvest.

They are at their best from Maine to Ohio and south to Georgia. When our plants were in their third year we had the coldest winter on record. Temperatures fell to −25° F, and I expected the autumn olive to suffer or die because I had read that they can be damaged by temperatures lower than −20° F. But the following spring they produced abundant foliage as well as bloom.

They need well-drained soil, but aside from that will flourish on a wide variety of soils. Set plants in the spring, six feet apart. If they are set in a hedge row, use the autumn olive as the tallest plants. Plants are available from nurseries, and an effort should be made to buy varieties adapted to your regional growing conditions. When they are a few years old, they will begin to produce pale yellowish flowers and clusters of fruit, which may be available to hungry wildlife anytime from July to October.

Quail Management

People who buy country places, especially through the southeastern states, often hope to have quail. The bobwhites that whistle from the fencerows on summer days form coveys in the fall, enticing confirmed quail hunters to the fields. The number of these birds available in autumn depends on how well they are provided for during the summer months. Land can be actively managed for quail production.

In top quail country, in good seasons, there may be populations as heavy as one bird for every two to four acres. A quail for every ten or twelve acres is still a population heavy enough to support hunting without threatening the next season's crop. Thin cover can be a limiting factor. Good cover may include cropland, woods, grassland, or brushy areas. But a major point made by the wildlife managers is that all these elements, as well as good food and ample water, should be found by the birds in fairly close proximity, so they will not have to travel far from the area where they hatched. This bird needs open areas for scratching and a variety of plants for feeding. Seeds make up about 80 percent of the quail's annual diet. It feeds on natural foods along field borders and the edges of woodlands, as well as on waste grain in corn, soybean, and grain sorghum fields. It also favors lespedeza plantings.

Watering places near good cover and food will benefit not only quail but also many other wild species. Water can be provided in anything from a small pond to the lid of a garbage can. Where you can spare the water, a hose dripping into a shallow pan or a plastic-lined pool can become a heavily used wildlife attraction.

Have More Rabbits

Rabbits are popular around the farm, as long as they do not nip off the buds of trees and shrubs during the winter or invade the garden too often in summer. Studies done in Missouri show that the female cottontail normally has six or seven litters a year, giving birth to four to six young at a time. In addition, about a third of the young females will have young of their own during their first summer.

Obviously, a lot of these rabbits are never going to live to be old. If they did, the countryside would be up to its ears in rabbits. Holding them in check are natural factors such as heavy rains that drown them in the nests, predation by foxes, owls, hawks, and other species. The number of rabbits surviving is directly related to the quality of their environment, and the farm's carrying capacity can be improved for rabbits.

They must have three essential elements in their habitat. One is escape and concealment cover. Another is a good food supply through every season of the year. Then, they need suitable places for their nests. These must all be close together because rabbits usually live out their lives within 100 yards of where they are born.

Food plots planted especially for rabbits should be small— about $\frac{1}{10}$-acre each. These should be fertilized, plowed, and disked, then seeded in late summer to mixtures of grasses and ladino clover. Summer food plots can offer the rabbits a mixture of soybeans, dwarf milo, and mixed cowpeas.

The best nesting areas are often those found in thick growths of grass on well-drained areas that will not be burned, grazed, or flooded. Instead of burning brush, leave it in piles around the farm. Several small brush piles provide better rabbit protection than one giant pile.

Overall, the best way to make the farm more productive for wildlife is to view it as an ecosystem. Keep the welfare of wildlife in mind whether the job at hand is harvesting timber or plowing a new field. If you must burn fields or fencerows to clean them up, be sure this is done in late winter or very early spring when nests will not be destroyed. Clean farming is not good wildlife farming. Leave the fencerows to grow. If you take a harvest of timber, leave the old hollow trees standing, for den trees. Foresters may argue against leaving these old trees. But if you want to have wildlife, leave them anyhow.

Swamps, marshes, and wet meadows are often highly productive of wildlife. Leave them too, if you can, for the ducks, shorebirds, bullfrogs, and dragonflies because they give variety to the landscape and add interest to your days on the land. Of the 127 million acres of wetlands that once dotted this country, half have now been drained. And with the water went the wild creatures dependent on it at some stage in their life cycles.

Farmers fond of wildlife shun poison sprays. There are few such chemicals that take only the target species.

All kinds of wildlife are dependent on finding the habitat that will supply its requirements the year around. Farming is basically a system of reshaping and replacing natural habitats to make the land serve the needs of people. But farmers, and especially those owning small farms, can manage their fields, woodlands, and wetlands with the wildlife in mind and still reap the benefits of country living.

CHAPTER
26

FRIENDS AND WILD ENEMIES

Frontier codes were once applied against predators on farm and ranch. And coyotes may still be shot for simply being where a gun will reach them, while hawks (all of them living now under federal protection) are still killed and sometimes hung on barbed-wire fences as a warning to all "chicken hawks." Man, the supreme predator, condemns lesser predators to death, sometimes out of habits passed down through generations and accepted without serious question.

Some cases of predation on domestic animals cannot be doubted. My father was death on weasels because they invaded the chicken yard. There dashing, sausage-shaped predators could slice the throats of chickens far beyond their need for food, leaving the chicken yard littered with dead and dying pullets. My father's standard cure for all such natural enemies larger than potato bugs was his 12-gauge double-barreled shotgun.

But attitudes are starting to change, even among those making their living off the land. Wildlife on a farm is an indication of the health of the ecosystem. Except in extreme cases, wildlife is best managed with tolerance.

In some areas, coyotes and eagles still stand condemned, not for the harm they really do to poultry or sheep so much as for the killing someone thinks they might do. Thousands of wild animals killed annually may be doing man more good than harm. Eagles were killed in large numbers in the past by trapping, shooting, and poisoning. But eagles are a natural control for jackrabbits, which consume large tonnages of forage that could otherwise go to cows and sheep. Even in this age of federal protection for eagles, some ranchers continue to kill the giant birds. The coyote too is a mighty enemy of small rodents. A few enlightened states have turned their old predator control practices around. Instead of blanket condemnation of an entire species, they seek out and kill only the individuals found guilty of destroying property. Such selective predator control, where predator control seems essential, is wiser than the outdated vendetta against predators in general.

Some much smaller problem creatures threaten the peace of rural property owners. Bugs and other pests even become arguments against owning country property. But these pests cause stress out of proportion to their physical threat. Because they are widely viewed as problems, however, and sometimes *are* genuine problems, they deserve to be discussed.

Garden Pests

Rabbits are cute, raccoons are appealing rascals, and deer are gentle and desirable neighbors until they begin to destroy your garden, fruit trees, or shrubbery. The best course of action, when feasible, is to relax and enjoy the wild animals with which you share the countryside, if they are taking only a small toll of the garden.

But animals that have found a garden may consume much of the crop, sometimes in a few nights. Under those circumstances the gardener finds it difficult to enjoy these wild pests. Fortunately there are methods that seasoned gardeners have found reliable for combatting them.

The major threat to gardens and shrubbery comes from rabbits, mice, raccoons, deer, moles, woodchucks, and even the lowly box turtle.

Deer, mincing through the garden of a summer night, can trample ripening crops. But fortunately they can be kept out of the garden with no big outlay in cash or labor. One idea is to suspend aluminum pie plates on strings around the garden on the theory that these metal flashers, turning in the wind, will spook the nervous deer and keep them at a distance. Most gardeners, however, do not place great faith in this device. Most effective is a strip of chicken wire lying out flat on the ground around the garden so deer must step on it to reach the plantings. They dislike walking on strange surfaces.

But perhaps the best of all is blood meal, a powerful repellent to deer. It can be spread fresh after every rain either around the perimeter of the garden or right in the rows, where it supplies plant nutients as it breaks down without any damage to plants. Small cloth sacks (Bull Durham sacks are excellent), filled with blood meal, can be hung in fruit trees at about belt level where deer will get the scent as they approach the trees. One sack will protect a small tree, while you may want to hang several sacks of these repellents on your larger trees.

There are also repellents available for protection from rabbits. Rabbits can be heavy eaters in the garden. The repellents used include blood meal, wood ashes, raw ground limestone, red pepper, and tobacco dust. Or you can buy commercially prepared rabbit repellents. These can be either spread on the ground or used to impregnate a small rope, which is stretched around the garden on stakes three inches or so above the ground. Some gardeners successfully fence rabbits out by erecting a 30 inch-high chicken wire fence around the garden. It should be tight and preferably have the first inch buried in the ground. Keeping the weeds, grass, and brush cleaned out around the garden will reduce the appeal of the area for rabbits and perhaps cut back on damage to the garden.

Woodchucks enjoy garden produce tremendously, or so it would appear. Woodchucks live beneath one of our farm buildings. All summer long we see them come and go between their cool burrows and the garden. Under these circumstances, groundhogs are sometimes trapped, shot with rifles, or gassed with hose connected to the exhaust of car or tractor and inserted into the burrow for 15 minutes, with engine running. Shooting them with a rifle is probably the most effective control, and this is legal in most places if they are destroying property.

If there is one garden crop that will bring in the foraging raccoons from all around it is the tender sweet corn as it comes into the milk stage. Raccoons, discovering such a treasure, will proceed from stalk to stalk, sampling each new ear as they come to it. Tying the family dog beside the garden for the night may drive them off, at least until they learn the measure of his chain. Pole lights may work for a while, but raccoons become accustomed to them. Some gardeners go so far as to paint all ears of corn with ground red pepper mixed in vegetable oil. Others install transistor radios in the garden and serenade the wild things with hard rock to which the animals also become accustomed.

But the most reliable protection against raccoons, skunks, and woodchucks is the electric fence (see section on Fences).

Bees and Wasps

Bees and wasps terrorize some people, becoming a physical threat as well as a stress factor. But before a wholesale campaign is begun to eliminate all these stinging insects from the property, slow down long enough to consider their role in the local ecosystem. Many are hard-working predators that kill insects to feed their young. The victims of hornets include house flies, blow flies, and caterpillars, while some wasps specialize in killing garden pests including armyworms and corn earworms.

But sometimes bees, wasps, and hornets must be brought under control around farm buildings, around the yard, and along paths. Our old farm house had gone unoccupied for two years before we moved in, and during that vacant period had become a center for wasps and mud daubers, especially in the attic. This situation is common around old buildings.

Nests of these insects may be above or below ground, depending on the species. Yellowjackets usually build their nests in the ground, although they may establish a colony in a hollow log lying on the ground. Bumblebees are also underground dwellers. Hornets and mud daubers nest above ground. Mud daubers build their adobe structures around buildings, and the hornets select a location either in shrubbery or on a protected part of a building.

If you plan to destroy a nest with a chemical, wait until after dark to spray. Dust can be sprayed into the hole of ground-nesting bees. Cover the entrance with a shovelful of earth so you can keep the insects in where the poison will reach them. Within 24 hours the colony should be eliminated. Liquid formulations can also be poured into the hole. A recommended chemical for ground-nesting bees is Sevin.

The best season for killing bees and wasps, hidden inside walls or partitions, is spring when the insect numbers are at their lowest for the year. Mud dauber nests can be safely knocked down during the winter to cut down populations the following summer. Paper wasps and hornets use their nests only one year. Mud daubers are rather gentle creatures and seldom sting a person unless touched or caught in clothing.

Swarming bees are generally not a great threat to people unless they are molested. The workers fill their stomachs with honey before leaving the hive, and this tends to keep them calm. They will usually not stay more than a few hours in any open location. Unless you want to keep them yourself, the best answer is to call a local beekeeper, who may want to install them in one of his hives.

Snakes No Big Problem

One reptile I was sure would live on our place was the copperhead. A friend who is a herpetologist has long had a love affair with copperheads. He collects them and keeps them in cages in his basement at home, and his most productive collecting grounds are in the county where we bought land. But we still have not encountered a poisonous snake here. The only snakes we see are harmless consumers of mice, insects, and other creatures considered by most people to be enemies of people. Our favorite reptile is a hognosed snake that lives beneath a wood pile beside the old chicken shed. I have surprised it often out sunning in the open. But regardless of its puffing and bluffing, it cannot be aggravated into striking people.

These and other experiences over the years have convinced me that people worry too much about snakes. Some people have an almost unnatural loathing for reptiles. We have friends who refuse to hike in the woods except in winter. This is precaution out of proportion to the threat.

There may be a snake out there, and probably is, but this fact alone should not discourage anyone from owning a country place and enjoying it. We hike our land the year around, although we usually wear high boots and long pants. The best protection is common sense. Take care whenever walking in snake country. Never place your hands on ledges you cannot see, and watch when stepping over logs in the woods or moving stones or logs. Unless you surprise the serpent, your chances of being bitten are small indeed. Snakes are eager to get out of your way.

If you are bitten, kill the snake for identification, keep quiet and have a friend go for medical assistance or rush you to the hospital.

Are Mosquitoes Necessary?

Mosquitoes have few defenders. When they are abundant, they can turn a pleasant experience into a miserable one. They may be especially troublesome around the yard when you want to sit outdoors or have a picnic. On occasion, they may transmit malaria or equine encephalitis to people, or heart-worm to dogs.

Mosquito experts will tell you that there are many kinds. Wisconsin, for example, can claim some 40 species. To the average person a mosquito is a mosquito, and none is welcome.

The most effective time to attack mosquitoes is when they are in the larval stage. At this stage they are living in water as "wrigglers." Deny them wet places to reproduce and you cut down their populations. They may find water in unexpected places. Old tires that collect rain water become excellent refuges for mosquito larvae. So do empty tin cans, stock-watering devices that are not in use, rain barrels, bird baths, gutters, even saucers in which house plants are watered. Fish pools will harbor fewer mosquitoes if there are fish in them because the fish eat mosquito larvae. So do mallard ducklings.

Water is important to mosquitoes because the females lay their eggs on water or in places that may become flooded later. A productive female mosquito may produce from 50 to 200 eggs in a batch and lay several batches before the season ends. But before laying eggs she must have a meal of blood, which she sucks from the body of a warm-blooded animal. The larvae hatch two or three days later, feed on organic matter, and a week or so later change to pupae. A couple of days later the pupae change into adults, and the cycle is ready to begin another round.

If you have a lot of mosquitoes around the farm, keep a container of insect repellent handy. This will hold them off for up to five hours. Some formulations, however, as the labels will warn, can damage plastic materials including eyeglass frames, cameras, and watch crystals.

Chemical fogging is sometimes done around vacation areas. Fogging machines can sometimes be bought in hardware stores, but this system of mosquito control is only justifiable in extreme situations.

Another technique to avoid is the use of persistent insecticides. In the past, large areas have been indiscriminately sprayed to the detriment of entire ecosystems. Wherever insecticides are used, extreme care is called for to keep from over-dosing the environment and damaging wildlife, soil, and water sources.

Ants and Termites

Nobody has to go to the country to find ants. But, because ants are sometimes listed as arguments against visiting the country, I'll include them in this country rogue's gallery.

Usually the only damage they do is the infestation of food. There is one exception: the carpenter ant. If you find large black ants, they are likely carpenter ants. This is a bad sign because carpenter ants chew up wooden walls and insulation in homes, not for food as the termites do, but to create nesting places for raising their young. They usually begin by invading a decayed place. The ant colony, once established, creates its ideal living conditions. Enough moisture is generated to keep the wood-destroying fungus growing. In time carpenter ants can cause widespread damage to a building.

They may find their way into the house first in firewood. Or they may begin where water leaks through and soaks the wood, places such as windowsills, pipes, and chimneys. Correct the cause of the rotting wood and you have taken a major step in bringing the carpenter ants under control. After sealing off their homestead and drying it up, treat the colony with an application of insecticide purchased especially for the purpose from your supply store.

Winged ants sometimes cause panic among people convinced that termites have invaded. Catch one and you should be able to tell whether it is a termite or winged ant. Termites have thick waistlines and front and rear wings that are about the same length. Flying ants have thin waistlines and their front wings are much longer than their rear wings.

Poison sold for ant control, placed near where the ants travel should bring them under control. Sprays and dusts can also be bought at local stores. Be certain to get those intended especially for ants, and to use them sparingly, carefully, and according to directions.

Poison Ivy and Oak

For some people a real enemy of fun in the country is poison ivy. The poison carried by this plant and its relatives, poison oak and poison sumac, affects some people severely, others not at all. But even those who believe themselves immune should take precautions against poison ivy. Authorities say there is no such thing as true immunity. The best protection is to learn to recognize poison ivy, oak, and sumac, then avoid it. Children should be taught to recognize it also, because some children are especially susceptible to plant poisoning.

Poison ivy always has three leaves. It produces clusters of small white berries. It prospers along old fencerows, rock walls, roadsides, and trails as either a shrub or vine.

Poison oak also has three leaves in a group. The undersides of these leaves are whitish. It is usually not a vine. Pacific poison oak, which may be found through most of California and the western half of both Washington and Oregon, is often found growing in woodlands and along roads, mostly as a shrub. Leaves are glossy and leathery in appearance and grow in threes.

Poison sumac, which grows from the Gulf Coast to the Great Lakes and eastward to the Atlantic, is a small tree or shrub. Usually it is found in bogs or swamps. The compound leaves have 7 to 13 leaflets arranged in opposing pairs. Other sumacs can be easily told by the color of the berries. The harmless species have clusters of red berries, while poison sumac has clusters of white fruit.

Poison ivy can be carried in a number of ways. Dogs, cows, and other domestic animals, rubbing against the plants, may transfer the poison to people who touch them. If poison ivy burns, the smoke may carry the poison. It is most likely to cause poisoning in spring and summer when the plants carry an abundance of sap. Never let even the oldest "expert" tell you that the way to gain immunity to poison ivy is to chew the leaves.

Poison ivy can be controlled, and where it grows close to dwellings or outbuildings, it should be killed. There are three ways to do this. One is to clip pastures and fields where it grows. But a plant allowed to grow for a couple of months has roots well enough established to grow back even if the top is clipped. Frequent clipping will be needed to kill it. It can be successfully grubbed out, preferably when the ground is wet and easy to dig, but the entire root must come out. This is not a job for short-handled tools unless you are truly immune.

As a last resort, chemical sprays can be used to kill the plants. Agricultural extension people recommend Amitrole and ammonium sulfate, applied with a small pressure type sprayer on a quiet day in spring or summer. Low pressure, forming large droplets, is better than a fine mist under high pressure for the protection of nearby plants. For killing individual plants around yard and out-buildings you can use a small spray can from the local supply store.

Poison ivy should be recognized and respected, but it should not be a deterrent to enjoying the country.

Health and Hazards

Weekend farmers will do well to check their schedules with a doctor. Many of us spend five days of the week sitting on an office chair, failing to exercise from one weekend to the next. Then we rush into a flurry of physical labor—building fences, cutting firewood, and working in the garden. It's fun, but it could be hazardous.

Most doctors advise that this weekend exercise is not enough to keep the body in top condition. Instead, they urge mature people to exercise in the middle of the week as well. A regular exercise program strengthens the body, adds to its ability to perform work, and, some say, adds time to a person's life.

Farm tasks can be as demanding as a fast game of basketball or touch football. A heart specialist might suggest a stress electrocardiogram for the weekend farmer. It is important, say the physicians, to understand that any strenuous prolonged exercise can be a potential hazard to the person unaccustomed to such work.

No matter how much work there is to do in Spoon Hollow I mix it with relaxation. I may stroll up to Pine Pond to see what new migrating ducks have arrived, or sit on the porch and listen to the whippoorwills.

CHAPTER
27
THE IRS AND OTHERS

The Internal Revenue Service has a guide designed to help farmers fill out their complicated tax returns. Ask for the latest edition of Farmer's Tax Guide. If you intend to operate the farm as a profit-making project, you will want to take all allowable deductions.

For both the owner and the IRS, the question is not as simple for the city resident who also owns a farm as it is for the person whose farm is his business. The big question becomes whether the farm is *intended* to be a profit-maker. The IRS does not insist that it make a profit every year. Farms often fail to turn a profit in a given year. But if the farm rocks along year after year without making a profit, the owner has no basis, at least in the eyes of the IRS, for continuing to claim that it was intended to make a profit. At some point it becomes officially a hobby farm, and deductions for operating it are no longer allowed.

The usual stipulation is that the farm must make a profit two years out of five, or in the case of horse farms, two years out of seven.

An official of the IRS, in a major field office, explained that the operation does not have to be broken down into activities, with every major operation showing a profit. The farm, she explained, is figured as a single operation. The hog operation can lose money indefinitely, she replied, as long as the business as a whole shows a profit two years out of five. If, after five years, the IRS rules that it is a hobby farm, the finding is retroactive and all deductions taken on it over the years will be disallowed.

There is also a provision for requesting a delay in the judgment of whether the farm is a profit-making enterprise. This may go on for five years or more while IRS specialists watch your operation for signs of profit or no profit.

If you are farming for profit, and therefore involving the IRS in your program, detailed records become as essential as for any other business. Such records are not only to give information to government agents if they should demand it but also to guide you in the regular operation of your farm.

The record keeping should be done regularly throughout the year because you may need to estimate what your taxable income is going to be at various times other than when returns are due. By figuring your approximate taxable income, you can—if you choose—adjust your income and expenditures in time to alter the total tax picture. For example, you may find that your income is going to be uncommonly high and therefore hold off selling cattle until after the first of the year to transfer that portion of your income to the coming year. Or you may want to increase your deductible expenses ahead of the year's end. On the other hand, if your records reveal that your income from the farm promises to be low for the year, you may want to speed up sales to spread out the income.

Allowable deductions, if you farm for profit, include depreciation of farm improvements, machinery, and purchased livestock. Your farm records should show details on such property including: 1) date purchased, 2) cost, 3) years of life, 4) method of depreciation, 5) depreciation claimed to date, 6) possible salvage value, 7) investment credit claimed.

Farmers have a choice of using either the cash or accrual basis in keeping records and filing their returns. But the choice is made at the time the farmer files his first tax return on the farm operation. It thereby becomes the system with which he must work thereafter, unless given special written approval by the IRS to change. The cash method is simpler because there are fewer records involved, and inventory accounts are not needed. The advantages of the accrual system may include spreading out the taxes where one year brings heavy costs, but the sales do not come until the following year, as can happen with certain grain and livestock operations.

Your county Extension Service office will probably be able to supply account books for keeping your farm records, as well as the IRS Farmer's Tax Guide for the year.

Giving Land Away

If you own land that includes an unusual bog, swamp, forest, prairie, desert, or piece of tundra, you may want to think about passing your holdings on in a way that will preserve its natural features. Naturalists in your state conservation agency will probably be happy to walk over your acres with you and help identify natural features of lasting interest.

One national organization formed to identify such acreage and promote its preservation is the Nature Conservancy, Suite 800, 1800 N. Kent St., Arlington, Virginia 22209. The Nature Conservancy began in 1950 when a group of professional ecologists decided that this country's natural areas were slipping away at such a pace that something must be done quickly if significant areas were to be saved. Since then the group has grown steadily.

Field workers for the Nature Conservancy are experts in advising land owners about the best way to save natural areas of true merit. There are a number of ways to go about this. One is to make an outright gift and deed the land to the Nature Conservancy or some other agency, allowing them the choice of what purpose it will serve best.

Another method, and one with special appeal to some landowners, is to execute a standard deed but retain lifetime rights to occupy and use it.

Also used on occasion is a deed with restrictions written into it. In this case the organization receiving the gift, understandably, may want to include provisions that give it some control over uses of the land that might destroy its natural value.

All such donations can offer tax benefits to the landowner giving his land away. According to the Nature Conservancy, a gift of land to a charitable organization, approved by the Internal Revenue Service, carries the possibility of a substantial reduction in federal income taxes. The deduction may be limited to 30 percent of the taxpayer's adjusted gross income in any given year, but such benefits can be spread out over a period of several years. Under some circumstances, it is possible to reap more benefit from such a gift than it would be to sell the land outright. The government does not establish the value of such a gift. This is up to the owner and the findings of the professional appraiser he employs. Large industries know this technique and in recent years have found it to their advantage to make contributions of holdings that have special value as ecological areas.

A fourth method is to write the gift into your will. Instead of having an immediate tax benefit, the gift could make substantial reductions in estate and inheritance taxes. If you do consider writing such a bequest into your will, it is best to consult with the organization in advance. This approach allows experienced people the opportunity to help you work out any bugs in the plan and prevent problems at a later date.

The best course of action for landowners, thinking along these lines, is to contact the Nature Conservancy or other agencies that might accept their gift.

Share Crops and Tenants

If you buy a farm with tillable acreage, you may want to grow crops for profit. This can be a sound idea, even on a small farm. But before buying machinery to do the work yourself, you should give it some thought. The idea may appeal, but the crops produced may not support the machinery investment.

A better answer will probably be found in a straight rental or share-cropping arrangement if you can find a nearby farmer to work the land for a share of the crops.

If your farm has tillable land and a house suitable for occupancy, you may rent the farm. You are fortunate if you find a capable young farmer who is not yet financially able to own his own land, and wants to begin by operating as a tenant. The businesslike way to go into such an agreement is with a written lease, giving both parties a full picture of what each can expect.

Obviously, the potential income from the farm will be a major factor in striking a deal with a good tenant. The farmer needs enough productive land and suitable buildings to carry out a profit-making enterprise. Farms of 180 acres or more with good buildings will be more attractive to a tenant than smaller farms. If your farm is small, you may simply choose to rent out various fields on a share or cash basis. Good buildings may also be rented by neighboring farmers either as part of the land rental agreement or separately.

Where you work out a share lease, the expenditures should also be shared in the proportions in which the income is shared. The owner contributes the land, the tenant contributes the labor, and beyond that you will have to split expenses.

When you go into such a plan, a map of your farm is a definite aid to its management. It should show field boundaries, drainage, soil tests by fields and years, when lime was applied and amounts spread, plans for current crop program and soil treatment, and a record of annual crop yields. Both parties should keep a copy of the map.

Honesty and mutual trust can make such an arrangement a pleasure instead of a bitter experience. On occasion, both parties must be willing to negotiate in reasonable fashion because they are in business together and both have substantial investments in time or money. This feeling between owner and tenant can lead to long-term arrangements, which are preferable for many reasons to dealing with a succession of tenants. But the agreement might best be made first for one year, with renewal automatic unless one party notifies the other, in writing, of the intention to discontinue the agreement. This notification usually comes two or three months ahead of the renewal date, and the date for termination is normally part of the written agreement.

Before signing on a new tenant, check around. If he is widely known as the poorest farmer in the county, a poor credit risk, lazy, or possessed of notably poor business judgment, you should know. In addition, his family will be part of the picture and have a major role to play in keeping the property neat and attractive, as well as in getting the work done. The tenant farmer's wife is as important to the operation as she would be if the family owned the place. If you can line up a first-rate young tenant who wants to own his farm as soon as he can swing the deal financially, you are probably better off to take him on even if he will last for only a few years, in preference to a less-qualified operator who might stay with you longer. Profit for both parties is the aim, and the good farmer, with respect for the land, can help you build the farm no matter how short the time he works with you.

Absentee owners with larger acreages, especially those having trouble with operating the property or not well acquainted with the problems of farming, may want to turn the task over to a professional farm-management service. Before making such a deal, you would do well to check around with owners who have employed these services.

Coping with Vandalism

Friends of ours have a weekend farm some miles away in the southern part of the county. There they raise a fine garden and maintain a network of nature trails where they and their guests like to hike. One autumn morning they drove out to their farm to harvest sweet potatoes, which they had carefully tended. The idea was a good one, but the timing was bad. Someone had already been there and dug up the crop.

Other friends even had the windows taken from their old farm house. Often the vandalism takes the form of destruction rather than outright stealing. Broken gates, windows, and equipment are common complaints of absentee land owners, and this is a problem faced by owners of rural property in every part of the country.

Rural sociologists say flatly that vandalism is increasing in rural areas and speculate on the reasons. They point to a breakdown in respect for property, more one-parent homes, more free time and easier transportation for high school students, and a failure of parents to instill in their children an appreciation for property rights.

More by luck than planning, we found our place back on a lane that dead-ends after winding a third of a mile from the public road. Anyone getting in there without a neighbor's knowledge would have to walk where there are no trails through thick woods and heavy brush. Road frontage increases property values, but we have been happy to be situated far from the public road, out of sight of those who might be bent on mischief.

Aside from location, there are obvious steps to take as protection against vandalism, such as shutters that can be locked on windows. Heavy gates with chains and locks will discourage a proportion of those who might otherwise enter. Signs warning against trespass may be helpful part of the time. But these are only protection against the honest people. The sheriff of our county assures me that security lights in the yard are a big help, and so are lights with timers in the house.

But the best protection is a good relationship with your neighbors. When you buy the old place, people living nearby wonder what the new owners will be like. Country people are not pushy about forcing themselves on new property owners in the neighborhood. But if newcomers make a point of getting acquainted with the neighbors, they are usually welcomed. You will have occasion to seek the help of local people, especially when it comes to hiring someone with a tractor or disk to help get the garden worked up, or perhaps to seek advice on timber cutters, or where to find a reliable well-driller. The better acquainted people in a neighborhood are with you, the more they are likely to keep an eye on your property if you are away. Even as a new property owner, you may have opportunities to help the neighbors in a tight spot, not because you expect anything in return, but because old-fashioned neighborliness still has a place in pleasant country living.

Owning Land

All of us who own land must remember that we possess it for only a little while. It has been written that we do not inherit the land from our fathers but borrow it from our children. In the nineteenth century, a Blackfoot chief responded to an offer to buy tribal lands by saying, "Our land is more valuable than your money. It will last forever. It will not even perish by the flames of fire. As long as the sun shines and the waters flow, this land will be here to give life to man and animals. . . . As a present to you, we will give you anything we have that you can take with you: but the land, never."

The inner satisfaction coming with ownership of land grows, in part, from the ability to improve it. Owners of rural property everywhere sense that caring for the land enriches the experience of buying and enjoying a small farm.

Government Help For Rural Landowners

AGRICULTURAL STABILIZATION AND CONSERVATION SERVICE

The county Agricultural Stabilization and Conservation Committee administers federal agricultural programs at the county level. "Cost sharing" is one of these programs that provides financial assistance to landowners who carry out certain conservation practices such as tree planting, new permanent seedings, and pond construction. Other ASCS programs include grain price support, storage structure loans, wool incentives, "natural disaster" assistance for feed grains and wheat, tobacco quotas and/or allotments, and indemnity payment programs for milk producers and beekeepers.

EXTENSION SERVICE

The Cooperative Extension Service, a part of the State University, is an educational organization with professional staff in each county. Its chief responsibility is to provide research-based information on all aspects of farming and country living.

FARMERS HOME ADMINISTRATION

The FHA of the U.S. Department of Agriculture provides financial assistance to farmers for a variety of projects. For example, a loan could help a family buy or operate a farm, or acquire a home.

HEALTH DEPARTMENT

Local health departments are responsible for protecting public health. Non-resident landowners get assistance in making major improvements in home water supply or sewage systems, and permits for disposal systems. Calling on the local health department early may save the landowner major problems.

SERVICE FORESTRY PROGRAM

Service Foresters assist private landowners, as well as wood-using industries, with advice on reforestation, forest management, timber harvesting, merchandising, and forest tax laws. These are cooperative federal-state programs.

SOIL CONSERVATION SERVICE

The Soil Conservation Service, an agency of the USDA, assists landowners with soil and water conservation projects. Working through local Soil and Water Conservation Districts, SCS assists individuals in developing conservation plans for their land, including the "best use" for different classes of land, desirable pond locations, and ways to increase farm productivity.

SOIL AND WATER CONSERVATION DISTRICTS

Soil and Water Conservation Districts (SWCD) are independent bodies responsible for conservation of soil and water resources within their boundaries (usually coinciding with county lines). Each is governed by an elected board of supervisors.

The district's major function is to determine soil and water conservation problems and design and implement programs with SCS technical assistance.

INDEX